Foreword by Sue Beer, EFT Four

First Aid for Feelings

The essential Manual for self-care skills and good health

Thor A Rain with Nicki Hayes

First published in Great Britain in 2023 by The Helpful Press.

ISBN: 978-1-7395630-0-4 (Paperback)

　　　978-1-7395630-2-8 E-Book)

　　　978-1-7395630-3-5 (Audio)

British Library Cataloguing-in-Publication Data

A catalogue record for this book is available from the British Library

Photo credits: Andrea Bulcock (p.viii) and Holly Singh (p. ix)

Cover and book design by Berenice Howard-Smith, Hello Lovely

Proofreading by Annie Deakins, Proofnow

Printed and bound by Ingram Spark

The Helpful Press, Future Business Centre, Kings Hedges Road, Cambridge CB4 2HY UK

Contents

The First Aid for Feelings **Manual** is dedicated to Jenny Wade.

Jen came to a First Aid for Feelings workshop in 2015 just as Thor was setting up The Helpful Clinic as a social enterprise. At the end of the workshop she invited Thor for a meal and said, *"How can I help make this available to others?"*. She became an advisor to The Helpful Clinic and a dear and loving friend to Thor.

Jen passed away unexpectedly in 2020.

Her guidance, her vision, and her care continue to be present in every word and every action.

Here's to curiosity & compassion
May you find it helpful

Thor & Nicki

Foreword

As co-founder of The EFT Centre, Trainer, Mentor and Practitioner, to mention a few hats, I am always looking for new and better ways to explain the mindbody connection and teach my students and clients how to connect, or indeed reconnect, with their bodies and their feelings. Nearly two decades of searching for a palatable and practical answer have taught me three things are needed. Firstly, my attention needs to be grabbed and held on to. Secondly, I need some humour, while, thirdly, the elusive resource needs to be serious but not patronising. I can barely convey my pleasure to discover this book is all of these. Thor and Nicki have absolutely nailed it with First Aid for Feelings.

It was in my capacity as trainer of EFT that I first met Thor.

I was soon struck by their way with words and relish for a decent metaphor, and how this comes through in a learning setting as humour that educates! Once in a very long while I have come across the gift of the student you don't really need to teach – whose innate and acquired wisdom, and ability to communicate it, brings the whole class up. Thor is one such! Over time, and as Thor's mentor, I have witnessed their growth, personally and professionally, not least in establishing the Helpful Clinic and the very first First Aid for Feelings workshop.

If I was happy to be invited to write this foreword actually reading the book produced sheer delight. First Aid for Feelings is a manual which will teach you everything you need to know to understand your feelings – what they are and how to manage them. It will teach you to understand how you think and therefore behave. It is profoundly simple. It should be delivered to every home, school, and GP practice in the land, immediately. It is essential reading and I speak as the one who has searched for such a resource for decades.

Each chapter builds from simple to quite complex or advanced self work.

There are simple but highly effective breathing exercises and explanations for how and why they work. Memorable phrasing and languaging stick like earworms. You can be curious to meet your crocodile, acknowledge your brain is a three-scoop ice-cream, get sherlocking and triangulating and go forth to your bright new future. With your well-stocked First Aid Kit for Feelings your life will never be the same again. And, more to the point, anxiety and overwhelm will never be the same again.

Thor is one who has walked this path before us so they not only walk their talk but have been back to dismantle the paving and forensically examine the terrain. The manual is a testament to its source, its voice is that of a clear and trusted guide. It would simply not be possible to write so clearly on the subject of health and emotional literacy without an intimate knowledge and understanding of the subject. The ability to communicate that to others is what makes this book seem like a purpose fulfilled. Thor and Nicki deliver the promise of far better days ahead for anyone who engages with this book.

I am so glad to have had the opportunity to write this piece and be involved in some small way with the birthing of First Aid for Feelings **Manual**. You can probably tell I am a fan, and I will not hesitate to recommend it to all my students and clients – it deserves to be required reading for all medical students and health practitioners. But most of all it speaks directly to you, perhaps on your own at home and feeling anxious and overwhelmed. First Aid for Feelings can give you what you need, a manual that is a lifelong friend, a well-thumbed resource with the power to ignite your own internal flame.

Sue Beer, EFT Founding Master

London, May 2023

About the authors

Thor A Rain
(They/them)
MA (Hons) Dip.Clin.
Hyp.NLP.Coach.EFT

Thor (They/them)

"I help people feel better"

Thor A Rain is a health activist, pain and fatigue specialist and a social entrepreneur. They've helped thousands of people feel better mentally, physically, and socially. They themselves have recovered from complex PTSD, ME/CFS and Fibromyalgia – having been told by doctors they'd never recover.

It was during their recovery that Thor developed the First Aid for Feelings method, including the **ABC** technique and the First Aid Kit for Feelings. Once recovered they completed a Master's degree and a clinical diploma, which included Clinical Hypnosis, Neuro-Linguistic Programming (NLP), Emotional Freedom Technique (EFT) and Coaching. Working with patients, Thor realised that the First Aid for Feelings method was helpful to others. After working with this method in consultations since 2010, Thor taught the first workshop in 2013.

Galvanised by patients' successes, Thor set up a social enterprise in 2015 to help others, called The Helpful Clinic. The clinic's social mission is to improve people's health and well-being by increasing health and emotional literacy. This is done through consultations, workshops, meditations on the Insight Timer platform, and publications like this First Aid for Feelings **Manual**.

Nicki Hayes
(She/her)

"I help people communicate better"

Nicki (She/her)

Nicki Hayes is a freelance writer specialising in well-being and social impact. She has been a companion to many authors and organisations in these areas, contributing to six books to date. She has also been involved in many psychology-based development programmes, delivered both online and in person. Topics include life skills for young prisoners; employment skills for the long-time unemployed; and evidence-based behavioural skills for living well with anxiety.

Nicki has a strong sense of social justice and interest in social impact. She's written for organisations such as Cambridge Social Ventures and Pioneers Post, and mentored purpose-led entrepreneurs on the 50th Generation programme. Authoring countless articles about values-led business, she's also helped many social entrepreneurs find their "Why bother?" and shape how they tell their stories.

In the absence of telepathy, words and actions are all we've got to understand ourselves and each other. So, for Nicki, words are where it's at. Easing the suffering of miscommunication is her "Why bother?".

Introduction

What is the First Aid for Feelings Manual?

This manual, much like a traditional First Aid Manual, gives practical advice on how to respond to different situations. Rather than specifically relating to medical situations though, the information and advice provided here focusses on helpful ways to respond to physical sensations and emotions. By "physical sensations and emotions" we mean feelings and the thoughts that can go with them.

What is First Aid for Feelings?

First Aid for Feelings is a method that helps you respond to your feelings in the moment and in real-time. Its primary purpose is to be practical and it includes concepts, tools, and techniques. Just as with medical first aid, once you know how to use it, it's a rapid response that you can apply in any given situation when you experience intense feelings that you struggle with.

What First Aid for Feelings is not

There is no claim that First Aid for Feelings is going to radically transform your life or defuse highly-challenging situations. It isn't a cure. It won't replace speaking to a professional or getting medical help. It won't, in and of itself, resolve underlying physical, mental, and social experiences. Neither will it fix situations and relationships that you struggle with. It will help though.

Why a First Aid for Feelings Manual?

So, why a manual about First Aid for Feelings? Well, because feelings are information and, when you don't know what they mean or how to deal with them, you struggle. Our hope for you is that when you finish this book, you will understand the clues that your feelings are giving you and feel confident responding to them.

Why learning to understand the clues your feelings are giving you can be helpful

Feelings are an integral part of self-care. In fact they are the clues that let you know what self-care you need. Self-care is knowing what you need, when you need it, and being able to do something about it. If you didn't have feelings you wouldn't know how to care for yourself. This is essential when it comes to your health.

Why self-care is essential for good health

When you're able to read and respond to your feelings and your self-care is solid, you can address issues that arise with your health early, before symptoms get worse. Early intervention can make a critical difference with most health issues.

Even if you're dealing with ongoing health issues, your feelings and your self-care will help you manage and ease wherever possible the impact of that experience.

The relationship you have with yourself is the only relationship that is with you every breath of the way, from your first to your last, and every hour of your day. Your feelings, your self-care, and your health are vital to the well-being of this most important relationship of all, your own.

Our wish for you

By developing and strengthening our self-care skills, we've both seen our relationships with ourselves become sturdier, more resilient, and more enjoyable. That's not all though. We feel the benefit within our physical, mental, and social health, including better relationships, too. Actually, our entire quality of life is just so much better because we feel better. And this is what we wish for you.

What will you learn?

- How understanding the purpose of feelings means you no longer get stuck and can respond to your feelings appropriately and move through them

- How to know if you are struggling with your feelings, what your feelings are trying to tell you, and how you currently respond or react to your feelings

- Your **ABC** for Feelings, a new technique which is just as important as the **ABC** (**A**irway, **B**reathing, **C**irculation) for medical first aid, and which will help you respond helpfully to your feelings

- A way of thinking of the brain that will help you to see when the oldest part of your brain is in control. The part that is more primal and less rational. Knowing this creates the possibility for you to be kinder to yourself and more skilled with your feelings.

- How the practice of breathing mindfully helps to release stress and improves your ability to think more clearly

- How taking time to learn what your feelings mean, and what they are communicating, gives you the clues and power to respond better to your feelings, and make more helpful choices towards what you actually want

- Why, if you feel that you don't have any choice, you are "crocodiling". And how soothing your crocodile reconnects the part of your brain that can see and make choices.

- Why curiosity makes it easier to respond to intense feelings and take helpful action

- How being kinder to yourself helps you be more skilful and compassionate with yourself, as well as with others

- How to start building a First Aid Kit for Feelings and set yourself up well for whatever comes your way.

How did the First Aid For Feelings concept come about?

Thor first developed the First Aid for Feelings concept back in 2003 when they were severely ill. Diagnosed with Post-Traumatic-Stress-Disorder or PTSD, ME/CFS and fibromyalgia, they'd been told in no uncertain terms that they would never recover. Dealing with the relentless pain and fatigue — as well as the anger, overwhelm, and anxiety — inevitably took its toll.

More often than not they would be frustrated with themself for handling these experiences unskilfully. They remember thinking, *"I'm a reasonably intelligent person. How come when I'm struggling, I forget even the most basic things that I know are more helpful to me?".*

Learning about how the brain works, Thor slowly began to recognise that feelings are important, even when they are uncomfortable. They are important because they give us vital information. Thor realised that understanding why feelings "show up" meant that they could access and use this information. This gave them the power to take more helpful action based on those feelings.

Thor's first lightbulb moment

It was a lightbulb moment when Thor realised that chasing the "good" feelings whilst ignoring the "bad" was actually unhelpful. The relentless messages to "be positive" and the belief that if they focussed hard enough on telling themself they'd recover, they'd miraculously make that happen, meant they had snookered themself. They'd snookered themself because they were missing out on the valuable information that the "bad" feelings contained.

Thor's second lightbulb moment

Then came a second lightbulb moment: realising that "feelings" were both physical sensations and emotions, and that the two were connected. You can't have one without the other.

Being originally from Iceland, where equality is one of the highest cultural values, it made sense to Thor to treat all feelings equally.

Surely being able to draw on the diversity of feelings they were experiencing was a good thing? So, they started on their quest to understand their own feelings and solve the clues these feelings were giving them. Treating all feelings equally, whether they were pleasant, like joy and pleasure, or unpleasant like shame or pain, was the key to cracking the code that eventually helped Thor recover.

The understanding that came with these two insights made Thor realise that they had been practically illiterate when it came to their health and their feelings.

Curious and keen to learn more, they realised that these insights are integral to something called health and emotional literacy. This is something that has become a hotbed for research in the last decade.

Perhaps the most widely-known researcher in this area is Brené Brown, whose wise words, such as those shared below, continue to inform and enlighten our approach.[1]

> "When we don't have the language to talk about what we're experiencing, our ability to make sense of what's happening and share it with others is severely limited ... Language shows us that naming an experience doesn't give the experience more power, it gives us the power of understanding and meaning."

We then take this further with our inclusion of physical sensations, alongside emotions. Physical sensations, like pain and fatigue, are essential to being able to address what's going on physically and therefore bring in the aspect of feelings in health literacy.

The balancing act

More about health and emotional literacy in Chapter two. Before progressing further though, let us say a little about positive psychology. Many of the techniques that have evolved from it are super helpful. Associated research by Martin Seligsman, the Godfather of Positive Psychology, and colleagues, for example, has been invaluable.

When it first became a "thing", positive psychology was very focussed on strengths, and we're sure that you have seen strengths-based approaches to personal (and team) development work well. We both certainly have. But what happens when people (including ourselves) become too focussed on what we think is positive? Well, in our experience, the actions we then take can be like sticking a plaster on a bruise. Sure, we've taken action and done something, but has it actually addressed the issue?

The power of the "yes, but"

Focussing on positive self-talk, for example, can lead to people ignoring the vital information that their "yes, buts" are giving them. First Aid for Feelings does not ignore these "yes, buts". Instead, it encourages us to listen to them and, rather than judge them, to get curious[2] about the information they are trying to tell us. More often than not, the "yes, but" is pointing to an unhelpful belief or dynamic with somebody or something else. This could be "You're not good enough", or the fact that you don't have the skill yet to do something, or that you may need additional help to move forward.

By taking your "yes, but" seriously and addressing it directly you can transform the "yes, but" into "yes, and" making what seemed impossible not only possible, but probable.

Trying to navigate feelings using only one dimension — the positive on — is a bit like rowing a boat with only one oar. It takes a lot of effort and you may even move forward at times but overall you're likely to be going in circles.

First Aid for Feelings provides a method to help you work through your "yes, buts" and find your way forward to your "yes, ands".

Whilst First Aid for Feelings wasn't the only aspect to Thor's recovery, it was the everyday tool that helped them stay on track and steadfastly move forward. Two decades later, they still use their First Aid for Feelings. They find it helpful, and they are not alone in that.

Indeed, at the time of writing this book:

· More than 500 people have attended First Aid for Feelings workshops

- More than 7,500 one-to-one sessions (including many ad-hoc sessions during COVID-19 lockdown) have been delivered

- More than 2,500 people have signed up for the First Aid for Feelings 10-Day Meditation Course on the Insight Timer app. The course launched at the start of the COVID-19 lockdown and is consistently rated 4.7 out of 5 stars, with student numbers continuing to grow

- All in all, more than 5,000 people have benefitted from learning First Aid for Feelings to date.

Thor specialises in working with pain, fatigue, stress, and anxiety and has been working in that field since 2010. They set up The Helpful Clinic as a social enterprise in 2015 with the mission to improve health and well-being through increased health and emotional literacy. These last 10+ years, they have become increasingly convinced of the role of health and emotional literacy in reducing the risk and impact of pain, fatigue, stress, and anxiety escalating in the first place.

> **To quote Desmond Tutu:** *"We need to stop pulling people out of the river. We need to go upstream and find out why they are falling in."*

How Nicki got involved

Encouraged by the success stories of those who use this approach — many of which we share within these pages — creating this manual seemed like the next logical step to Thor. Chatting it through with Nicki, who they had first met when Nicki interviewed them about setting up The Helpful Clinic back in 2015, Thor realised they had found a strong ally.

Nicki's daughter had been diagnosed with ME/CFS, and, as her school's response to this diagnosis felt inadequate, Nicki had decided to remove her from mainstream education. Doing so was absolutely the right thing to do. Yet, it added another role for Nicki, that of "homeschooler", to her already complex self-employed, single-parent lifestyle. Using some of the methods that we share here helped to support Nicki through this challenging time.

Nicki had also rolled up her sleeves and got stuck in volunteering at Thor's first impactathon in 2016. This is where 25 socially-minded people gathered to develop the First Aid for Feelings training material. Leading a team of six, Nicki was instrumental in designing some of the First Aid for Feelings exercises we include here. She also had valuable knowledge and understanding to contribute, having helped a range of authors write books about strengths-based psychology and emotional fitness over the previous 10 years.

What is the purpose of First Aid for Feelings?

First Aid for Feelings has three main functions:

1 To enable you to make more helpful choices when you go through the challenges that happen in everyday life

2 To help mitigate and take the intensity out of an experience or situation until more long term support can be put in place. It can prevent experiences and situations from becoming increasingly more unhelpful

3 To help support symptoms, recovery, or personal development, alongside talking and / or physical therapy.

Why is First Aid for Feelings helpful?

Most of us don't consciously have a method for managing our feelings and coping with stress and stressful experiences. When we struggle with the intensity of our feelings, we tend to "reach" for things that may give us temporary relief, like we would reach for plasters and paracetamol. Things such as sweets, food, and drinks. Or substances, such as caffeine, alcohol, cigarettes, and drugs. Or activities, like exercise, sex, overworking, gambling, or social media.

We even have behaviours that give us temporary relief. We push through. We speed up and rush. We procrastinate. We focus on other people's feelings and problems rather than our own. Whatever it is that we do, all too often we just keep on doing it without considering whether it's helpful or not.

Of course, sometimes we know what's helpful, but when we're in the thick of it, we just don't remember it or do it. Research into why this happens is becoming more focussed.

Why do we forget what is helpful, and reach for or do stuff that really isn't?

We are more likely to reach for an unhelpful response to our feelings when we are in an adrenalised state. This state, which we refer to as the "stress state" throughout this book, can affect our working memory as well as impairing our access to our long term memory. This means that we can't access the skills and the knowledge that we store there. The stress state is essential for our survival, but it can also limit our ability to think straight and make helpful choices. We'll explain why and how in Chapter three.

Because your ability to think straight is affected in this way, First Aid for Feelings is vital to your well-being. It means you're much more likely to be able to access the more resourceful part of your brain, which enables you to make more helpful choices.

What is a First Aid Kit for Feelings?

Now that you know what First Aid for Feelings is and what it isn't, let's look at the First Aid Kit for Feelings. Much like a medical first aid kit, the First Aid Kit for Feelings is a place where you put together useful tips, tools, and things that you can turn to when you are struggling.

Many of us have some painkillers, maybe some anti-inflammatory tablets at home. We'll have some plasters, maybe bandages and antiseptic cream too. Most of us know that it helps to have it in one place. This means that when, for example, we cut our finger, we know exactly where to go to find what we need. This stops us from charging around the house and bleeding all over the place whilst rummaging in drawers and cupboards, trying to locate the plasters.

Most of us know what a First Aid Kit is and that it has things in it. We don't give it a second thought that someone had the idea to put these things together into a kit, or that someone came up with the name "First Aid Kit". You wouldn't think that it's only been around since the late 1800s. It's kind of obvious, right?

Why don't more of us have a First Aid Kit for Feelings?

That's a question we often ask ourselves, and one of the reasons we decided to write this book. Having what you know is helpful to you in a place where you can easily reach for it, means you can look after what you need, when you need it.

Many of us know what helps us in some situations, yet do not have a kit that has everything we could need for all the feelings we struggle with in one place. Know the expression: "Out of sight, out of mind"? Well, the reverse of it is also true: "In sight, in mind".

In sight, in mind

By exploring and noticing what is helpful and putting together your very own First Aid Kit for Feelings, you consciously grow your ability to comfort yourself, soothe your hurts, reassure your doubts, motivate yourself when you need it, and do what's in your best interest.

How to use this book

This book is a manual. Like all manuals, it provides step-by-step instructions. It also provides true stories about people who have used the concepts, techniques, and tools to help themselves feel better and be more skilful in dealing with others. It is intended to be used as a manual upon first reading, i.e. step-by-step and section by section.

You will learn the **ABC** of First Aid for Feelings, how to recognise what's going on, and how to respond to it well. Ultimately, you arrive at Chapter ten, where you start to build your own kit.

We recommend that you read through the book in the order it's written. Settle in a place where you know you are comfortable and will not be disturbed. Take notes in whatever way feels most helpful to you, be that in a notebook, notes function on your phone, or even in the margins of this manual. Use multi-coloured pens, make a cup of something lovely, put some music on, whatever helps to make this a nourishing experience.

Once you have read through this book, you can dip in and out of chapters on an "as needed" basis, in much the same way as you would with a medical first aid manual.

What to expect

As you progress through this manual, you will strengthen your understanding of your feelings and what they are telling you about yourself, your body, and your health. You will learn, practise, and then master the essential skills of self-care and good health.

Just like learning a new language, it's important to start with the basics and progress from there. To start with, you are likely to learn some basic nouns, like "bread" for instance. It won't be long before you're ordering a wholemeal baguette with sprinkles on top, but there will be a few steps and stumbles along the way.

As you begin to read through these chapters, keep in mind that you don't learn to swim by watching a documentary. The same applies with learning First Aid for Feelings. This stuff doesn't work if you only read the book. You need to actually do it.

We've written the chapters to make it straightforward and practical to use. Each starts with outlining what you are about to learn. You'll then read about someone who's used what you are about to learn, and how it helped them. Then we explain the thinking behind the exercises you are about to do (we call this the philosophy section). Next comes the exercise (the practise section), followed by the story of the person you met at the start of the chapter in more detail (the proof).

The chapters correspond to Thor's First Aid for Feelings 10-Day Meditation Course on the Insight Timer app. It also includes an extra chapter explaining how to build your First Aid Kit for Feelings. Supplementing your reading with these meditations is not essential, but it may help you to absorb and implement what you're learning.

Go gently, hold steady, stay the course

Thor often says, "The slower you go, the faster you'll get there". In essence, this means that when you try to do things too quickly, you're more likely to miss important details and it will take you longer in the end. As you prepare to read Chapter one for the first time, remember to be gentle with yourself. Give yourself time to begin your learning, and to build your own First Aid Kit for Feelings.

It's OK if things don't go to plan. It's OK to step away and to come gently back as and when it's helpful. We are all different. We all come across different hurdles along the way. The key is to go gently with yourself, hold steady, and stay the course.

One final word. A lot of the content in this book is informed by research in the fields of neuroscience, psychology, cultural studies, and health. Research is an ever unfolding field of curiosity and learning.

We are continuously updating our perspectives, metaphors, and conclusions from the research as we become aware of it. Sometimes the research has been superseded by more up-to-date information and we've decided to keep the original perspective because it feels helpful in practical terms. When this happens, we'll let you know and explain why we've kept it.

Neither Nicki nor Thor are professional researchers or medics. It's likely there's research that we're not aware of that will influence what you're learning here and how we present that. We acknowledge and value the knowledge, wisdom, and insights of the research that we use and quote in this book. Any errors or misinterpretations are ours. We are always open to new information and corrections if needed.

Wishing you warmth and wonder on your way.

Thor (They/them) and Nicki (She/her)

Chapter 01

What will you learn?

What feelings are

How you know you are experiencing a feeling

Why you are experiencing a feeling

How to chart your feelings so that you can understand the clues they are giving you

Why allowing feelings to take over, or avoiding them altogether, is unhelpful

How everyone has a feeling style and what influences yours

Why it's worth bothering to learn and do your **First Aid for Feelings**.

01

Jane's story (She/her)

Jane suffered from recurrent kidney infections. She'd tried everything to cure them before learning about First Aid for Feelings. By getting curious about how she was feeling, she realised that she was almost continuously in a state of overwhelm. Then came the insight that, because she felt overwhelmed so much of the time, she tended to ignore messages from her body. These two revelations led to some simple behavioural changes and a turning point.

Jane has been free from kidney infections for five years thanks, in part, to what you are about to learn. At the end of this chapter, you can read her full story.

Philosophy

What actually are feelings?

In order to do First Aid for Feelings, you first need to understand what feelings are. We're here to tell you that feelings are information. If this sounds obvious, banal, or trite, take a breath and read on. If this doesn't sound like any of these things, take a breath anyway and read on ...

> **Feelings — by which we mean both physical sensations and emotions — show up to give you valuable information.**

Note that we're defining feelings as both physical sensations and emotions. So many of us are so used to splitting our experiences into "mental" and "physical" the fact that they are related passes us by. Understanding that physical sensations and emotions are different expressions of the same phenomena — feelings — is central to the practise of First Aid for Feelings. It will enable you to take care of all of your feelings, all of the time.

How do you know that you are experiencing a feeling?

So far you've learnt that feelings are information and that they are both physical sensations and emotions. But how do you know you are having one? What is it that lets you know you're feeling anything at all? If you're feeling happy, or tired, or overwhelmed, or even in love, how do you know?

You may think it's obvious,*"Of course we know what we're feeling!"*. You'd be surprised though at how many people struggle to identify and name their feelings. One scientific study[3] suggests that around 10 percent of the population struggle with this. This matters because further research has shown that not being able to do this can lead to harmful behaviours, suggesting that the inability to name what you're feeling (the medical term for which is "alexithymia") is broadly associated with various mental and physical health problems".[4]

Think about that for a moment, "The inability to name the emotions that you're feeling is broadly associated with various mental and physical health conditions". Then consider how so much suffering could be avoided, if only everyone had the health and emotional literacy needed to name what they're feeling.

The six components of state

How do you know that you are feeling a feeling? Well, by reading the clues given to you by your thoughts, the tone of voice you are using, your emotions, your focus (in terms of time), your posture, and your physical sensations. Together they create the state that you're in.

Let's try it out, using the example of the feeling known as "joy".

Imagine feeling joy. Let's get curious about joy:

- What kind of **thoughts** are you thinking when you experience joy? What are the actual words that show up in your mind?

- What's the **tone of voice** that's speaking your thoughts either in your head or out loud?

- What does the **emotion** of joy feel like? What qualities does it have? How would you describe it?

- Where's your **focus** in terms of time? Is it in the past, present, or future?

- What's your **posture**? This is the body shape you're in when you're feeling joy

- What are the **physical sensations** you are experiencing? Where in your body do you feel joy?

Take a few moments to answer the above, then consider this: how do you know that this is the feeling of joy and not, say, hunger? How do you know the difference? And why does it matter? This leads us to the question, *"Why do you experience the feelings that you experience?"*.

Why do you experience the feelings that you experience?

Imagine if you couldn't tell the difference between joy and hunger. Life would be very problematic. Chances are you'd be scuppered, don't you think?

We can all be confident about why we feel hungry. It's to make sure that we get something to eat, otherwise we'd starve and ultimately die. This is important survival information.

The same applies to pain. Being able to feel pain is important for our survival. A few years ago, Thor sprained their ankle playing and running on ice. If the sprain hadn't triggered pain, they wouldn't have known there was an issue and very likely done further damage to their ankle.

Joy is something we all experience at least some of the time. Surely, just like hunger and pain, it's there for a reason? But what is the reason? Why would you feel joy? It doesn't prevent you from starving to death or alert you to threat, so why on earth would you feel joy? What wouldn't you know if you didn't feel joy?

Joy lets you know what you like and what you want more of. Chances are that without joy, you wouldn't know what you like. You wouldn't have a mechanism for distinguishing between what's helpful to you and what's unhelpful. You wouldn't be able to make choices about what to do more of or less of.

Because we're all different we can't say that the same experience is joyful for everyone. This means we can't make assumptions about what others find joyful. Thor, for example, finds joy in reading research papers because they like concepts, ideas, and "hanging out in their head". Finding joy for Nicki though, often means escaping from her head. She enjoys pottering in the garden and working with her hands, activities towards which Thor is wholly indifferent.

Next let's get curious about why we feel pleasurable feelings like joy.

Why do you feel pleasurable feelings?

It's often easier to understand why we experience feelings that give us pleasure. Love lets us know who we want to spend time with. Joy and pleasure let us know what we want more of. Laughter lets us know what we find funny, and so on. Most of us welcome pleasurable feelings, although some people do find those feelings difficult to handle and that's also important to know. Feelings are always information, even when we don't yet know how to interpret that information.

But what about uncomfortable feelings? Why do we feel them?

Why do you have uncomfortable feelings?

When it comes to feelings like anger, anxiety, overwhelm, guilt, or shame, we struggle, and find them uncomfortable. Some of us even go to great lengths to avoid them.

Apart from the obvious survival feelings like hunger and pain, why do we feel those unpleasant feelings? What could possibly be the point?

To get us started, we'll work through the feeling of overwhelm. Of course, other unpleasant feelings are available: envy, anger, anxiety, frustration, fury, rage, guilt, sadness, stubbornness, and shame, to name but a few. You'll get the opportunity to discover more about each as you work your way through this manual. You'll get to learn about the pleasurable feelings too.

As stated at the beginning of this chapter, all of our feelings — physical sensations and emotions — exist for a reason: to provide us with important information about what's happening to us. It is only by understanding the information that our feelings give us, that we're able to make the most helpful choices about what we need and what to do next. In a way, our feelings are like our own internal satellite navigation system, there to guide our needs and influence our next moves.

To help you better understand what we mean by this, we're going to explore a specific feeling in detail here — the feeling of overwhelm. We are going to do this using the six components of state you learnt about earlier in this chapter. Our intention is to give you a taste of what you can learn about all of your feelings as you progress through this manual.

Ready? Let's go ...

Why do you feel the unpleasant feeling of overwhelm?

How do you know that you are feeling overwhelmed? What are the thoughts in your head? What's the tone of voice that you're hearing these thoughts in? What are the emotions you feel? Where's your focus? Are you focussing on the past, present, or future? What are the physical sensations you are feeling? How do you know you are feeling them? What's your posture?

Overwhelm is often characterised by feeling stressed and speedy and feeling like there's just so much to do, in fact, more to do than you have time or resources for.

When you are feeling overwhelmed, you're probably struggling to think clearly, and even when you try to prioritise, it's like your brain is tripping over itself. You may find that you're rushing around, bumping into door handles, or furniture.

A classic example is searching all over the house for your keys and then discovering them in your pocket. This inability to think straight is one of the most frustrating things about overwhelm.

Let's chart the clues that tell us that we're experiencing the feeling of overwhelm.

Feeling chart

Thoughts

Typical thoughts people think when they are experiencing overwhelm include: "I'm running out of time"; "There's too much to do"; "Why am I so incompetent?"; "And another thing ..."; "Why do I always have to do everything?".

Or, if people are very overwhelmed they may not actually be able to make out the words in their head. It may just be noise.

Tone of voice

For most people experiencing overwhelm, their voice becomes rushed and agitated. For some it's like a constant murmur in the background. For others, it's like a high-pitched tone, or even like a silent scream.

Emotions

People experiencing overwhelm may feel bad about themselves, or angry that people keep wanting more and more from them. They may feel fearful that they're going to break. The emotion tends to have a constricted quality and is often described as bleak, heavy, or even like a fog.

Focus

This is about where we place our focus in terms of time. Are we focussing on the past, present, or future? People's focus when they are overwhelmed is most often on the near future, the next few hours, or days. Rarely do people feel overwhelmed about something that's already happened or about something that's expected in a few years time.

Physical sensations

Most people feel some of these sensations: tightness in the chest and across the shoulders; a knot in the stomach; shallow breath; headache; restless legs; agitation; needing to tap feet and / or fingers; tired sensations across the eyes; loss of appetite or strong craving for food.

Posture

The shoulders of people experiencing overwhelm are often hunched or folded over, their head is often either tilting downwards or a bit upwards, as if trying to keep their head above water. There's a contraction about the whole body, and movements can be jerky.

Figure 1.1 Feeling chart

What is the purpose of the feeling of overwhelm?

Given just how unpleasant overwhelm is, what could possibly be the logic or the purpose of this feeling? Let's recap ... this feeling shows up when there is so much to do, in fact, more than we have time or resources for. This is your clue. Overwhelm shows up when the triangle of time, tasks, and resources doesn't add up. Therefore, something needs to be addressed in order to respond to the overwhelm and move through it to a more helpful overall experience. One way to do this is by triangulating.

Triangulating your time, tasks, and resources

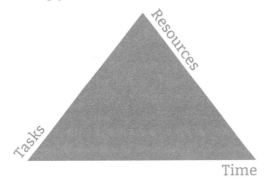

Figure 1.2 Triangulation

Let's look at each corner of the triangle in turn.

Task(s): What is the task that you're trying to complete? Are you trying to fit a task that actually takes six hours, into three hours? Does the task need to be done all in one go? Can you break it down into smaller and more easily achievable steps? Does it really need to be done to the extent that you originally thought? Is it helpful? What would be more helpful?

Time: What's the timeframe you've got here? Can some components of the task be moved to another day? Who do you need to speak with to negotiate that? You may not realise it but the first person to negotiate with is yourself. If the task doesn't get done by the time you originally set, what are the consequences?

Resources: Can you bring in some help to do this task? Can you buy in either someone else's time or tools to help make the task easier and quicker to do? It may not be obvious, but making sure you've got enough resources also applies to ensuring that you're getting enough sleep, water, and food. You wouldn't expect a car to drive without fuel, or a horse to race without rest, would you?

By getting curious about the clues that your overwhelm is giving you, you will find your way through, rather than going round and round in circles. However, whenever this feeling shows up, chances are it's important.

If it's a feeling that often shows up for you, there's sure to be important information that you've not yet got from it, or some action that you've not taken to address and move through it, yet.

A note on overwhelm about feelings

Overwhelm is almost always in relation to tasks and doing. However, we can sometimes feel overwhelmed by our feelings. Although that's not about "doing", so to speak, or "tasks", the same principle applies. When we are overwhelmed by our feelings, the clue is that it feels like we're feeling too many feelings at the same time. This means we can't process all of them and so tend to disconnect, which then means we can't process any of them. As you learn your First Aid for Feelings, you'll learn how to respond to this type of overwhelm and how to pace your feelings in a way that allows you to process and move through them.

What if you never felt overwhelmed at all, ever?

As you work through this manual, you will become familiar with the phrase, "It's more helpful to be curious than critical". In fact, the whole of Chapter eight focusses on why curiosity makes it easier to respond to intense feelings in ways that are helpful.

In getting curious about why we have feelings though, it's also helpful to consider what our lives would be like if we didn't have the feelings we're exploring. Let's consider this: what if we never felt overwhelmed?

Never feel overwhelm — ever? Your initial thought may be that this would be blissful, wonderful ... or would it? If you never felt overwhelmed, what would that tell you?

Chances are that you would be restricting your life to a clearly defined comfort zone, and not actively engaging with the fullness of living, with all its inherent uncertainty and potential. You might even be feeling other challenging feelings, such as boredom, or a lack of mojo.

Without the feeling of overwhelm, you wouldn't know what you are truly capable of, you wouldn't know the limits of your capacity and potential. Often, we don't realise just how powerful and capable we are until we learn how to recognise those limits for what they are.

Can the feeling of overwhelm be helpful? Absolutely! When the feeling shows up occasionally, rather than being like a default experience for you, it's helpful. If you're frequently or continuously in a state of overwhelm, it's not helpful and, if anything, it's costing you valuable resources and poses a risk to your health and well-being. More on that in Chapter four.

What can you do about it?

How can you chart your feelings so that you can understand the clues they are giving you?

As you work through this manual, you will, amongst other things, learn how to recognise the six components of state we introduced above and interpret the clues that your feelings are giving you. In fact, you are about to start by discovering how your feelings show up in all six areas for three important feelings.

Learning to identify and interpret feelings is a skill like any other skill. And, like any skill that you want to master, you need to invest your time and focus to not only learn but also to practise it. After all, like we said in the introduction, you don't learn to swim by watching a documentary. You'll get the idea and the rudimentary principles of swimming but you won't develop the ability to swim. The same applies here. If you just read this book but don't do the exercises, you'll get some benefit, of course. But it's unlikely that you'll develop the skill and the mastery to truly understand what's going on for you, what you need and what actions will move you forward to where you want to go.

01 First though, let's ponder on why you should bother learning to feel your feelings in a way that is helpful for you. Think about it, when you don't learn to feel your feelings, they take over, or you avoid them altogether, neither of which are helpful.

Why is allowing feelings to take over, or avoiding them altogether, unhelpful?

Recognising the clues your feelings are giving you, means you can choose how to respond to these clues in ways that are helpful.

When we don't know how to respond to our feelings well and don't know how to interpret the clues they give us, it can lead to difficulties at work, at home, and in our relationships. It can lead to difficulties with our physical and mental health too.

Here are some examples:[5]

· If you leave persistent symptoms unattended, they are likely to get worse. The risk here is that the medical intervention needed to deal with your symptom at that point is more intensive or invasive than it would have been earlier on

· Difficult feelings, like anger or anxiety, can escalate until they become destructive

· Behaviours like being late or snapping at people are likely to get worse

· Our friends, family, and colleagues are likely to find us difficult to be around and we are more likely to fall out with people

· Money can become an issue because you overspend or neglect your finances

· Our relationship with ourselves breaks down and we don't feel like we can trust ourselves, or that we're capable of looking after ourselves

· Our performance and ability to "do" and "deliver" is affected, which creates difficult consequences for us.

How do you start to recognise the clues your feelings are giving you? First you need to recognise your feeling style. Your feeling style describes the predominant way in which you experience your feelings. We all have a feeling style, and both nature and nurture play a role in establishing these.

What's your feeling style and what might have influenced it?

Different people have different behavioural styles when it comes to how they respond to their feelings. One way of visualising the behaviours we have is to see it as a spectrum. On the opposite ends of the spectrum you'll find **blockers** — people who numb and block their feelings — and **engulfers** — people who find themselves engulfed by the intensity of their feelings most of the time.

BLOCKER ←————————————→ ENGULFER

Figure 1.3 Feeling style

We all sit somewhere on this spectrum and we can all, at times, be engulfed by our feelings and at other times block our feelings. We can block some feelings, like anger, for example, but feel engulfed by other feelings, like anxiety. This is not a static experience. But it's likely that your default habit is either more towards blocking or more towards engulfing.

Remember, it's more helpful to be curious than critical. There will be a number of reasons for your feeling style. Some of them will be personal to you. Some will be what you've learnt from your childhood environment. And some will be cultural and influenced by the culture you grew up in. More about this in Chapter nine.

When we ask you what your feeling style is, we're not trying to teach you the "right" way to do feelings, or to shame you for doing feelings the "wrong" way. There is no right and wrong way. What we're asking you to do — and what this manual is designed to help you to do — is to understand your feelings and experiences. Doing so will help you to be kinder and more curious with yourself.

This manual will take you through a range of feelings, enabling you to recognise what feelings you're feeling and how to understand why specific feelings are showing up.

Whether you're a habitual blocker, a historical engulfer, or something in between, by working through this manual, you will learn this method. You will also learn how to build a kit of helpful resources that will be personal to you. This method and these resources will help you choose your response to feelings in a way that feels better than simply continuing as you've been doing. They will help you break any feeling habits you may have that are no longer serving you.

And, just in case you're not yet convinced, let's talk a little bit about your "Why bother?"

Figure 1.4 Why bother

Why is it worth bothering to learn and do your
First Aid for Feelings?

A phrase you will become familiar with as you progress through this manual is "Why bother?".

Many people dismiss this question claiming it's negative, standing in the way of achieving anything. We, however, feel that there is a difference between asking this question rhetorically, and asking it from a place of curiosity. After all, like the 80s pop song says, *"It ain't what you do, it's the way that you do it – and that's what gets results."*

When we say "Why bother" as if it has an exclamation mark at the end, it's rhetorical with no expectation of an answer. However, when we get genuinely curious about this question, it takes us to the very heart of the matter, as you will discover in this chapter's final exercise.

Are you struggling with a current situation in your life, like Jane who you met at the start of this chapter? Are you finding yourself in the same situation that you don't want, over and over again? Are you struggling with pain, fatigue, or energy levels? Are you feeling that everything is sort of OK, but it's like life's just missing something? Whatever your reason for learning your First Aid for Feelings and putting your own First Aid Kit for Feelings together, writing down what it is will help you hold steady and stay the course.

You don't need to know it exactly, and it doesn't have to be perfect or even make sense to anyone but you. This is your personal "Why bother?" and you can rewrite it as often as you like as you work through the manual and develop your skill and mastery.

Often, our initial "Why bother?" is not strong enough. There are two main reasons for this. The first is that people often think their "Why bother?" is something that they "should" do because it's good for them, rather than something that they actually want to do. This could be something like, for example, lose weight, stop procrastinating, or be nicer to people. This is unlikely to be a successful "Why bother?" because it's coming from a place of "should" rather than "I want". The "Why bother?" that comes from a place of should, comes from an inner critic perspective; more about this in Chapters three and nine.

The other reason why your first "Why bother?" may not be strong enough, is that you are doing it for someone else. This could be a romantic partner, your boss, a family member, or a friend. If this is the case, double check that this is a strong enough reason for you and that you are not just doing it out of compliance or obligation.

The final thing to note is that your "Why bother?" can change over time and that's a good thing.

Practice

Remember at the end of the introduction we encouraged you to go gently? Well, we are now encouraging you to do so with your first three exercises. You may want to sit down with a cuppa or listen to your favourite music while you do these exercises. You may possibly want to make sure you're in your favourite spot too. You may find that you need to read the exercises a couple of times and then sidle up to doing them. That's absolutely OK, whatever is most helpful to you.

Exercise 1.1: How do you know what you're feeling?

In this first exercise, you're going to start to get curious about some of your feelings, beginning with hunger, frustration, and boredom. This exercise asks you to get curious about how you recognise you're feeling these feelings. Sounds obvious, right? But you'll be surprised at what information and clues you can gather when you look more deeply and get your curiosity involved.

When it comes to feelings that you are struggling with, you may not realise that part of the struggle is recognising what's actually going on. These exercises are designed to help you to do that.

How does the feeling of hunger show up for you?

Component	Description
Thoughts	
Tone of voice	
Emotion	
Focus	
Physical sensations	
Posture	

Figure 1.1 Feeling chart

How does the feeling of frustration show up for you?

Component	Description
Thoughts	
Tone of voice	
Emotion	
Focus	
Physical sensations	
Posture	

Figure 1.2 Feeling chart

01 How does the feeling of boredom show up for you?

Component	Description
Thoughts	
Tone of voice	
Emotion	
Focus	
Physical sensations	
Posture	

Figure 1.3 Feeling chart

Exercise 1.2: What's your feeling style?

This is about getting curious about your habitual response to your feelings. Remember, it's more helpful to be curious than critical. Whatever you identify at this point will be the information that you'll use to move you forward from here.

Without spending much time analysing or trying to "get it right", put an X somewhere along this line where it feels relevant to you.

BLOCKER $\longleftrightarrow$ ENGULFER

Figure 1.3 Feeling style

Whatever style you have, it's likely that it's helpful some of the time and unhelpful at other times. What we want to work with is to help you work out when it's not helpful and then work out what would be more helpful instead, but, before you get to "there", you need to know what "here" looks like.

Remember that blockers will block, numb, or avoid feelings as much as they can and engulfers are more likely to be engulfed by the intensity of their feelings.

Exercise 1.3: Why bother?

Remember that it's important to have some sense of why you want to invest your time and focus to learn and practise these skills.

Take a few minutes now to ask yourself why you are bothering to step out of your comfort zone and into the unknown. Doing so now will help you find the clues you need to keep yourself motivated, hold steady, and stay curious.

My "Why bother?" is: ....

....

....

Exercise 1.4: Reflecting on what you've learnt

Now that you've thought about how you know what you are feeling, you've clarified your "Why bother?" and reflected on your feeling style:

- What was it like to do these exercises? For example, was it easy, informative, difficult, or confusing?

- What was it like to complete exercise 1.1? Have you ever thought about your experiences in this way before?

- Was it easier or more difficult to identify a particular component of state than another when completing exercise 1.1? Just to remind you, here are the six components of state: thoughts; tone of voice; emotions; focus (past/present/future); posture and physical sensations

- What did it feel like to put a mark on the blocker/engulfer line in exercise 1.2?

- What was it like to think about your "Why bother?" in exercise 1.3? Remember, your "Why bother?" can change over time.

What are you learning about yourself?

I am learning that I ....

....

....

....

....

....

Jane's story (She/her)

Jane, a single mum with a full-time job, suffered from recurrent kidney infections. She'd had support from her GP and a nutritional therapist and had successfully addressed many issues, yet was still getting kidney infections. The nutritional therapist referred her to The Helpful Clinic.

Completing the exercises above, Jane discovered that the agitation she felt most of the time was the feeling of overwhelm. She identified that when she was feeling overwhelmed, she ignored the messages her body was giving her, even believing that she didn't have time to go to the toilet.

We did an experiment to get information to help address this belief. Jane timed herself going to the toilet using the stopwatch on her phone. It took her less than three minutes from standing up to sitting back down at her desk. We then worked out that, even if she went to the toilet five times in a day, it would still be less than 15 minutes out of her day. This was a stark contrast to being off work for sometimes a week at a time with a kidney infection.

After getting curious and looking at how long things really took, it was a no-brainer. But she was stumped because she now struggled to recognise when she needed to go, so she put a timer on her phone to remind her to check in with herself. It took her a couple of months to retrain her body and her awareness. However, because her "Why bother?" was clear and the comparison of 15 minutes a day versus a week off work was an open-and-shut case, she stayed with it.

This, no doubt, contributed to Jane's kidney function improving. We also worked with other contributing factors like drinking enough water, becoming more active and triangulating her time / tasks / resources. As she learnt why she had feelings, how to recognise different feelings, and how to respond to them, there were also other improvements to her physical, mental, and social wellbeing. Her energy increased, her sleep improved, as did her relationships. The last time we checked in with Jane was five years after she came to The Helpful Clinic. She had not had a single kidney infection in that time.

01 Summary

In this chapter, you have learnt that:

- Feelings are both physical and emotional sensations that provide you with valuable information about yourself

- There are six components to feelings that help you identify what the feeling is you are experiencing: thoughts; tone of voice; emotions; focus; posture; physical sensations

- Often physical sensations and emotions are connected — understanding one dimension helps you to interpret the other

- Getting specific about what you are feeling, and how you know you are feeling it, means that you can address what you need and avoid things getting worse

- Asking yourself *"Why am I having this feeling?"* is helpful

- Asking yourself *"What information would be lost if I didn't have this feeling?"* is helpful

- It's more helpful to be curious than critical!

Next, keeping this learning in mind, you will begin to take a closer look at your current feelings and what you are doing now in terms of managing them.

Because we have introduced overwhelm already, the feeling most commonly named as problematic by people who come to The Helpful Clinic, we continue to work on it in the following chapter. As you progress further through these pages, you will have the opportunity to learn about and work with other feelings too.

Chapter 02

What will you learn?

In this chapter, you will learn:

Why you have feelings (and why it's important to understand the clues they are giving you)

Why seeing feelings — both physical sensations and emotions — as a language is helpful

What health literacy and emotional literacy are and why they're connected

Why it's important to ask: "Is it helpful?"

Why feelings are information

What lets you know you are struggling with your feelings.

By the end of this chapter, you will be ready to start learning the foundations of **First Aid for Feelings**.

02

Sukhi's story (He/him)

Sukhi carried a lot of responsibility at home and at work. He had felt exhausted for so long that he had lost the will to find a way to feel "normal" again. Until he learnt about First Aid for Feelings, he hadn't even identified that what he was experiencing was the feeling of overwhelm. Using the exercises in this chapter, Sukhi found his will and a way, which he called his "little and often" approach. Sukhi is confident in responding to the feeling of overwhelm now and using it as information.

You can read Sukhi's full story at the end of this chapter. His experience, when compared to Jane's in Chapter one, gives you an insight into how a feeling like overwhelm can be different for different people.

Philosophy

In the previous chapter, you explored the nature of feelings. You considered that feelings are both physical and emotional, and that physical sensations and emotions connect to and inform each other.

You began to explore how the feelings of hunger, frustration, and boredom show up for you. You might even have discovered that they are interlinked, that one drives the other, and that all are a result of physical, mental, and social influences.

The philosophy and premise of First Aid for Feelings is to always look at feelings (and health) in these three dimensions of physical, mental, and social. But it's not like we discovered this. It was first proposed in 1977 in a landmark article[6] published in the academic journal *Science* by a guy called Engel, who proposed the Biopsychosocial model of illness and health.

The Biopsychosocial Model of Illness

The Biopsychosocial model of health and illness is a framework developed by George L. Engel[7] in the late 1970s.

It proposes that all aspects need to be taken into consideration when attempting to understand and address health-related issues and symptoms. Arguing that biology is not independent of psychological and social factors, the model invites a more integrated approach to both the person experiencing the symptoms and the symptoms themselves.

With this model in mind, let's build on what you learnt in Chapter one.

Why do you have feelings and why is it important to understand them?

We often find that feelings get in the way. We may find ourselves thinking "how much better life could be" if we didn't have certain feelings. When we do that, we're missing the point though, which is that feelings are there for a reason: feelings are there to give us information about ourselves, who we are, what we like, what we don't like, and what we need.

Considering hunger again: why do we have feelings of hunger? Because hunger lets us know that we need food. If we don't feed ourselves, we can get so hungry that we lose consciousness and eventually die. In Chapter four, you will learn more about the evolution of the human brain, using a very helpful analogy of a three-scoop ice-cream,[8] which helps to explain this. Even without this knowledge yet in place though, it makes sense that eating is a basic need and the feeling of hunger helps keep us alive.

Why do many of us become irritable when we're hungry? Because we need food to survive. And, because when the oldest part of our brain kicks in (as it does when we're struggling), we get angry with anybody who gets in between us and the fridge. Ultimately, our body and brain are trying to prevent us from starving.

As you can see, even though hunger feels unpleasant, the mechanism is helpful to the body.

Consider next the sensation of pain. It's tempting to want to get rid of pain, right, but if you didn't actually feel pain, what would be the reality of it?

There is a condition called Congenital Insensitivity to Pain (CIP), which is considered life-threatening.

Take Ashlyn Blocker from Patterson, Georgia, who repeatedly hurt herself because she couldn't feel pain and didn't realise she was injuring herself.[9] One report shares how when she was young, she broke her ankle once and nobody realised for two days. Because Ashlyn didn't have pain as a teacher, she never learned how to move safely. Everyday activities that we take for granted pose a risk to Ashlyn.

Pain is information. If you don't have pain as a feedback mechanism, it's dangerous and ultimately works against you. Pain, like all other sensations, is information. It helps you to better adapt to your environment and to give your body what it needs.

Why seeing feelings as a language is helpful

As complex as physical sensations can be, emotions can feel even more puzzling. We often don't have the words to describe how we feel and sometimes we don't even know we're feeling an emotion at all. Learning to feel and name our physical sensations and emotions is like acquiring a new language. As Thor pointed out in the introduction to this manual, when you first learn French, you start with the word for "bread". You then learn the words for "wholemeal bread". Only later when you are confident do you learn to say "Wholemeal baguette with seeds on top". Your skill with the language, the grammar, and the vocabulary grows and deepens the more you learn, and the more you practise.

What we often don't realise is that emotions show up with their own physical sensations, and vice-versa. We can have a warm glow of contentment in our chest, or our head can feel like it's spinning with anxiety. It's the same with physical sensations. It's hard not to be frustrated when we're overheating or shivering with cold. Just like we often recognise an emotion because of the physical sensations, the emotion lets us know whether the physical sensation is something we like or don't like.

This kind of health[10] and emotional literacy, just like reading literacy, is learnt. We're not born with it, rather it's a skill acquired through learning and practise. If you do not feel very literate right now in terms of your health and your feelings, it's not because of a personality defect. It's simply because you've not had an opportunity to learn and practise. Would you expect to be able to read if you had not been taught how to do so? Probably not. So, don't be harsh on yourself if you're struggling to understand your feelings right now.

What is health literacy and emotional literacy?

Our view is that the two are connected and our approach is informed by a well-known therapeutic model: Steiner's 5 components of Emotional Literacy.[11] Steiner proposes that in order to regulate emotions effectively so that you can foster healthy relationships, you need to:

1　Know your feelings

2　Have a sense of empathy and achieve goals

3　Learn to manage your emotions

4　Repair emotional damage

5　Put it all together into "emotional interactivity".

First Aid for Feelings takes this into account, supporting you to create a safe place to learn and develop your health and emotional literacy. We know from experience that learning anything is easier when we get curious about it. It's our belief that it's more helpful to be curious than critical because that opens up questions and potential. Being critical, by contrast, tends to shut down the conversation, taking you down a feelings cul-de-sac, that is to say, it's just not going to take you anywhere.

With the principle of curiosity as our foundation, we invite you to embed into your daily routine a very important question, which is central to First Aid for Feelings: "Is it helpful?"

Why it's important to ask: "Is it helpful?"

When we look at how we think, feel, and behave when we are struggling, we often label our responses and experiences. It's important not to get caught up in what's good or bad, right or wrong, true or false, or even positive or negative. These ways of labelling our feelings tend to carry a lot of judgement. What in one situation may be considered a positive, might actually be unhelpful in another, and vice-versa.

> Rather than ask *"Is it good or bad / positive or negative / right or wrong?"* ask *"Is it helpful or unhelpful?"*.

We're prone to labelling feelings like jealousy, anger, and shame as bad, and feelings such as contentment, joy, and happiness as good. In our culture, there's been a big shift towards pursuing "good" feelings and to dismiss or ignore "bad" feelings.

However, there is a fundamental flaw in this way of thinking. All feelings, every single one of them, and we mean physical sensations and emotions, are there for a reason: to give you information that will enable you to meet your needs.

Next time you have a fèeling, ask yourself, *"Is it helpful?"*. Then ask, *"If I didn't have this feeling, what information would I be missing out on?"*. Then, keeping in mind your answer to this question, ask, *"What would be more helpful?"*. These are some of the key questions you will investigate in the next chapter where you will learn the **ABC** technique.

Don't worry if you don't figure it out straight away. It can take a while to train your mind to do this kind of thinking. Once you've got some clues it's helpful to experiment with how you choose to respond to your feelings, and act on the information they contain.

Why feelings are information

Feelings aren't facts. But just because they're not facts doesn't mean they're not valuable. They do have value. They provide you with information about what's happening for you in response to what's going on in the world around you. They also provide information about what's happening inside your own experience, physically, mentally, and emotionally.

When you're able to access your feelings and respond to them in a helpful way, you function and feel well. The first step to accessing your feelings is to become aware of them. Without awareness, you cannot take any action. The second step is to know what to call your feelings or be able to describe them. Without language or some reference to what this feeling feels like, you can't talk about what's going on, either with yourself or with others. This then gives you the understanding you need to be able to take action and address what the feeling is trying to let you know.

Spotting feeling patterns

You may have noticed that there is a pattern to, at least, some of your feelings. This means that some physical sensations, like symptoms and emotions, frequently show up in particular circumstances, or around specific people.

For example, maybe you have the pattern of saying "yes", when you want to say "no". Or, maybe you tend to get a headache when you're in noisy environments. Or maybe you feel clumsy around your boss, or feel vigorous after a walk along the river.

In the beginning it can feel difficult to spot patterns. We propose that you think of it like a game, a bit like the children's book "Where's Wally?". On the first page, it's really hard to find Wally. By the time you get to the last page, your eye is trained to find Wally and you're able to spot him more quickly and easily.

Whether you are aware of it or not, when you find yourself in situations that are challenging, stressful, or overwhelming, or around people that you find difficult, you always have some sort of a reaction. It therefore makes sense that we start by getting curious about how you're feeling in those situations, and the indicators that let you know you are struggling. Here's how you can create a profile for what's going on when a feeling arises. You will learn more about indicators in Chapter six.

Identifying the Feeling profile

The Feeling profile is a tool that helps you build up a profile of what's going on when a feeling arises. The Feeling profile compliments the Feeling Chart you learnt about in Chapter one and the sherlocking and map-making you'll be learning later in the manual. You'll develop the Feeling profile by answering nine questions. The answers you provide give you information about what's going on when that particular feeling arises.

Here are the questions:

1   *In what situations do I struggle with this feeling?*

2   *Are there particular people involved when I feel this feeling?*

3   *What is it that I "do" when I am feeling this feeling?*

4   *How do I know that I am struggling with this feeling?*

5   *What are the things I reach for when I begin to struggle with this feeling (such as food, alcohol, or overworking)?*

6   *What are the things I say to myself and the people around me when I feel this feeling?*

7   *How do I feel this feeling in my body?*

8   *How do I feel about myself when I begin to struggle with this feeling?*

9   *Is there anything else I notice about this feeling?*

Awareness is always the first step. Without being aware of what you're doing now, you're not able to make any changes. First Aid for Feelings is all about curiosity and compassion, so you're learning various ways of looking more deeply at your experience. You're now gathering information and the invitation is to do that without judgement. This is not about what you should or shouldn't have done. Rather, it's about "What's the information and the learning here?".

You'll then learn how to use the tools and techniques in this manual to help you make the changes you need. In the practice section you'll find an example of applying these questions to the feeling of overwhelm.

Figure 2.1 Feeling profile

Remember what we said about how you don't learn to swim by watching a documentary, you need to actually get in the water and swim? We encourage you to take this approach to getting curious about what you're doing now.

In the beginning it will take you ages, and you will, metaphorically, feel like you're staying in the shallow end. That's alright, that's an important part of the process. With practice, you'll progress and become more skilled.

Practice

What lets you know you're struggling with your feelings?

The following exercises are designed to help you learn how to identify and chart your feelings by looking at some specific people and situations that you're currently struggling with.

Before that though, let's start by identifying the feelings you feel most often: your habitual feelings.

Throughout these exercises, please keep in mind the helpful phrase we introduced you to in Chapter one: "It's more helpful to be curious than critical."

Exercise 2.1: What are your most habitual feelings?

Each of us tends to have a range of feelings we return to, again and again. These are our habitual feelings. This is completely normal, we all do it.

Let's start by looking at the most common feelings you experience.

Here's a list of a few feelings to help prompt you:

Fear   Boredom   Annoyance   Anger   Love   Hope
Desperation Worthlessness   Embarrassment   Hurt
Guilt   Shame   Frustration   Insecurity   Anxiety
Confusion   Bitterness   Jealousy / Envy   Lost   Inspired
Lonely   Miserable   Grief   Tension   Contentment
Trapped   Worry   Affection   Curiosity   Concern   Fury
Rage   Joy   Excitement   Anticipation   Devotion
Sadness   Stubbornness   Determination

Feeling description

1 Choose three feelings you experience daily, or at least most days. Write them in the first column below. We've included the example of overwhelm.

2 In the second column, note how intense each of these feelings feels for you on the scale of 0–10, where 0 = no feeling and 10 = as intense as it can possibly be. Note that the intensity can vary, but for the majority of people there's a range that applies at least most of the time. In the example we've included, the intensity varies from about 6 out of 10 to about 8 out of 10. It's not like it doesn't go below 6 or above 8, but most of the time it's in the 6–8 out of 10 range. You probably won't score the same intensity for each feeling.

3 In the third column, describe where in your body you feel the feeling the strongest. For example, you may feel the feeling of anxiety all over your body, but it's strongest in your chest, around your shoulders, and up into the back of your head. Use the words that make most sense to you.

4 In the fourth column, describe how the feeling feels, e.g. fast and overpowering. It's often helpful to use words that describe texture, like smooth, spiky, soft, and such like. Many people find it helpful to use colours (think "green with envy" and "feeling blue"). For some, feelings have sounds like humming or rumbling. And it's not uncommon that feelings have a "weight" to them, like it feels heavy or light. Use words that make sense to you.

Feeling	Score 0-10	Where felt in body?	Feeling feels like ...
Overwhelm	6-8	Jaw, back of head, shoulders, chest	Fast and overpowering

Figure 2.2 Feeling description

Exercise 2.2: Getting curious

Curiosity is the absolute starting point to making helpful choices. You will learn a technique called "sherlocking" to help you make helpful choices in Chapter six.

Taking the feelings you've begun to explore in the last exercise, let's get curious about what they might be about.

· Why might I have this feeling? If this feeling were to have a purpose, what might it be?

· What information would I be missing out on if I did not have this feeling? What would I do or not do that would be helpful or unhelpful to me if I didn't have this feeling?

Here is how we've done it, taking the example of overwhelm we used previously.

Feeling	Why might I have this feeling?	What information would I be missing out if I didn't have this information?
Overwhelm	Because I do not have enough time or resources to do the tasks I have to do.	I wouldn't know how much it's possible for me to do in a specific timeframe. I'd struggle to manage my own expectations, let alone other people's.

Figure 2.3 Feeling information

Exercise 2.3 Getting specific

Now let's pull this all together. Using any of the feelings you have begun to explore, complete the nine-point feelings profile below.

We have included one for the feeling of overwhelm as an example:

1 *In what situations do I struggle with this feeling?*

2 *Are there particular people involved when I feel this feeling?*

3 *What is it that I "do" when I am feeling this feeling?*

4 *How do I know that I am struggling with this feeling?*

5 *What are the things I reach for when I begin to struggle with this feeling (such as food, alcohol, or cigarettes)?*

6 *What are the things I say to myself and the people around me when I feel this feeling?*

7 *How do I feel this feeling in my body?*

8 *How do I feel about myself when I begin to struggle with this feeling?*

9 *Is there anything else I notice about this feeling?*

Name of feeling	Overwhelm
Situations in which I experience this feeling:	When I'm taking on new work roles or when I'm in a group setting.
People I struggle with then feel this feeling:	Everyone
What I "do" when I feel this feeling:	Panic
I know I'm struggling with this feeling because:	I start to lose things, like keys, my wallet, and my mobile phone.
What I reach for when I feel this feeling:	Lots of to-do lists, sugar, caffeine, and alcohol.
What I say to myself and those around me when I feel this feeling:	I can't cope. I'm stressed. I can't focus.
How do I feel this feeling in my body:	My jaw tenses. Tingling up the back of my neck. Heart races and shoulders feel tense.
How I feel about myself when I am struggling with this feeling:	I feel like I'm a failure.
Other things I notice about this feeling:	It's pretty constant.

Figure 2.4 Example Feeling profile

Name of feeling...	
Situations in which I experience this feeling:	
People I struggle with then feel this feeling:	
What I "do" when I feel this feeling:	
I know I'm struggling with this feeling because:	
What I reach for when I feel this feeling:	
What I say to myself and those around me when I feel this feeling:	
How do I feel this feeling in my body:	
How I feel about myself when I am struggling with this feeling:	
Other things I notice about this feeling:	

Figure 2.5 Example Feeling profile

Exercise 2.4: Reflecting on what you've learnt

Now that you've charted your feelings in these different ways, what do you notice about:

- What it was like to do these exercises? Was it, for example, easy, informative, difficult, or confusing?

- Whether it was easier or more difficult to identify the emotions or the physical sensations in terms of the different feelings?

- How aware were you before doing these exercises about your experience and the answers you've written down?

- Thoughts and ideas you're having about how you could respond differently to what's going on?

What are you learning about yourself?

I am learning that I ....

....

....

....

....

....

....

....

....

Sukhi's story: Little and often

Sukhi struggled with energy levels. Life's admin, including medical appointments, money, and housework, was creating such a feeling of overwhelm that he just couldn't move forwards. Task upon task piled up until he'd have to spend hours and hours sorting things.

Using the exercises above, Sukhi got curious about when he experienced this feeling and identified it as "overwhelm". By charting his recurring feeling, he saw that it was to do with how he balanced time, tasks, and resources.

Looking at his behaviour of leaving everything until it blew up and then spending a lot of energy cleaning up, he asked himself, *"Is it helpful?"*. The answer was no. When he asked, *"What would be more helpful?"* the answer was *"Little and often"*.

He realised that reaching for coffee and cake gave him sugar highs, followed by big sugar crashes, which left him useless for the rest of the day. This was not helpful. Neither was chastising himself for not being a real grown-up, or escaping into social media.

For Sukhi, the earliest indicator was a headache around his eyes. This feeling became his clue. If he got it, then, rather than reaching for coffee and cake, he would stop and reach for a pen and paper to write things down.

Sukhi realised that looking after life admin was just as important as looking after work admin. He decided to treat it as a job and gave himself half an hour every morning to do so. During this half hour, he would work through the to-do list he'd written. He felt he had enough internal resources to manage this amount of time. And indeed, it proved to be so.

Using the time, task, and resources tool introduced in Chapter one, and triangulating his time to look after the tasks that were causing overwhelm, Sukhi cleared the backlog. It took a couple of months to develop this little and often daily habit, and now that it is a habit, Sukhi very rarely gets to the point of overwhelm. You'll learn about how to make your more helpful choices a habit in Chapter ten.

02

Name of feeling	Overwhelm
Situations in which I experience this feeling:	When dealing with paying bills, on top of arranging medical appointments and just running my house.
People I struggle with then feel this feeling:	Everyone around me, but especially myself.
What I "do" when I feel this feeling:	Procrastinate, and worry, and dither. Then procrastinate, and worry, and dither some more ... And then do it all in one enormous big effort of a go!
I know I'm struggling with this feeling because:	I feel a headache around my eyes, tightening, like I have a band that keeps contracting.
What I reach for when I feel this feeling:	Coffee and cakes. Lots of social media scrolling.
What I say to myself and those around me when I feel this feeling:	I'm being childish. I can't do this grown up thing. I'm completely incapable.
How do I feel this feeling in my body:	I feel small and like I'm drowning or treading water. I feel a headache around my eyes. Also, the feeling feels fast and heavy.
How I feel about myself when I am struggling with this feeling:	I hate myself. I feel like I've failed to become an adult.
Other things I notice about this feeling:	Reaching for coffee and cakes gives me sugar rushes followed by sugar crashes.

Figure 2.6 Sukhi's Feeling profile

Summary

In this chapter, you have learnt:

- Why you have feelings (and why it's important to understand the clues they're giving you)

- Why seeing feelings — both physical sensations and emotions — as a language is helpful

- Why it's important to ask: "Is it helpful?"

- Why feelings are information

- What let's you know you're struggling with your feelings.

You are now ready to learn your First Aid for Feelings **ABC**.

Chapter 03

What will you learn?

Why the **ABC** mnemonic (Awareness, Breath and body, Choice) of **First Aid for Feelings** is as important as the **ABC** (Airway, Breathing, Circulation) mnemonic of medical first aid

What the most common thought patterns are for most people

How to identify your own thought patterns

How, when you are struggling with feelings and thought patterns, to use your breath and body to take you from where you are now to where you want to be

How to create helpful choices to take you to where you want to be.

Grace's story (She/her)

Grace's relationship with her mum had never been great, lately though, it was spinning out of control. Whenever they spent time together, Grace just could not get away fast enough. Using what you have now learnt, Grace became aware that she was struggling with feeling guilty. What you are about to learn in this chapter enabled her to regain control and rebuild a better relationship with her mum.

You can read Grace's whole story at the end of this chapter.

03 **Philosophy**

So far, you've begun to learn why feelings show up, why they're information, and how learning to deal with them is like learning a new language. Think of it as health and emotional literacy.

You've begun to develop your health and emotional literacy by exploring why you have feelings and how you know you are feeling particular feelings. You've learnt that feelings — and remember that feelings are always both physical sensations and emotions — connect to and inform each other. You've even begun to look at where you are with your own feelings right now.

Recognising and naming feelings is just the start of your First Aid for Feelings practice though, in just the same way as recognising symptoms is just the start of your medical first aid.

Medical first aid has a very well known **ABC** mnemonic, which stands for Airway, Breathing, Circulation. These are the essential first steps that medical professionals and first aiders check.

Such an "in the moment" response, used at the scene in an emergency to contain the situation until a medic arrives, has saved many lives. Our **ABC** mnemonic, which stands for **A**wareness, **B**reath and body, **C**hoice, is designed for use in emergency situations that relate to your feelings.

In this chapter, you will learn why this technique[12] is helpful and how to use it in your own First Aid for Feelings. The good news is that everything you've learnt so far in this manual relates to the first initial – **A**.

Yup, you've already started practising your **ABC**s! Before you move onto your **B**s though, it's helpful to reflect a little on why the **ABC** of First Aid for Feelings is as important as medical first aid's **ABC**.

Why is the feelings **ABC** as important as the Medical ABC?

The **ABC** Technique

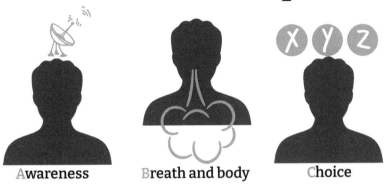

Awareness   **B**reath and body   **C**hoice

Figure 3.1 The ABC technique

Let's walk through the First Aid for Feelings' **ABC**, one step at a time.

Awareness

"**A**" is for "**A**wareness". This is about training yourself to be aware of the words you are actually hearing yourself saying, and asking yourself, *"What am I thinking, feeling, and doing?"*.

We're often so keen to move forward, make changes, reach goals, whatever it is, that we don't realise where we're actually at. And here's the thing about that: if you do not have a sense of where you're now before you think about where you want to be tomorrow, you're unlikely to get to where you want to be tomorrow. We refer to this as "Here before there".

In working through Chapters one and two, you have already started to think about your "here". You're becoming more aware of your feelings. In order to make the best use of this new level of awareness, let's get curious about some common thought patterns that most of us do at least some of the time.

03 What are the most common thought patterns for most people?

Every school of psychology, from cognitive behavioural therapy (CBT) to Transactional Analysis and Neuro-Linguistic Programming (NLP), to name just a few, talks about thought patterns. The list of such thought patterns is long.[13] However, there are seven thought patterns that most of us do, often habitually.

We can be doing these thought patterns in ways that are helpful, and in ways that are unhelpful. How do you know if it's helpful or unhelpful? Often, it's a case of asking yourself, *"Does thinking in this way make me feel good about myself, or bad about myself?"*

It's also about how often you are doing each type of thinking. If you've repeated the pattern three, four, or even five times — and you're actually moving your thinking forward — then it's probably helpful. If you're doing this type of thinking about the same situation more than five times — and it's not moving you forward, then it's not helpful.

Let's explore.

Mental tennis: *"Should I do this or that ...?"*

This thought pattern occurs when you are weighing up your options and making a decision or a choice. It's helpful to look at the benefits of something and get a sense of the cost.

Whether it's what to order on a menu or how to manage your workload, this thought pattern is helpful when done in moderation. It becomes unhelpful when you're stuck going from one to the other and back again, like tennis. When this happens, you're likely to either not make a choice, or do what you've always done before, even if it's not helpful.

Ruminating: *"If only I had ..."*

This pattern is about going over past conversations, events, or actions. Thinking about whether you are taking the learning from the past about what you need to do differently in the future to change things for the better, is helpful.

Whether it's a job interview, a presentation, an argument with a relative, or reflecting on how you could be more skilful can be helpful. After all, as Henry Ford famously said, *"If you always do what you always did, you'll always get what you always got."*

However, if you're just going around in circles, beating yourself up, there is no learning going on and so it's unhelpful.

Rehearsing: *"I'm going to ..."*

Rehearsing is about troubleshooting potential risks and issues, or doing thought experiments about how to improve a future event or experience.

Whether it's finding parking in a new town, or preparing for a tricky conversation, it can be helpful to plan the key points or aspects involved. This will help you identify what you can do to secure a better outcome.

When you're identifying information or actions to take, it's helpful. However, if you're doing the same thoughts over and over and not getting new insights, then rehearsing has become fear-based and you're now scaring rather than serving yourself.

Reference thinking: *"I can't do this because I have (or haven't) got the money / health / time / ..."*

This pattern is like a security system that runs continuously to evaluate your every experience from a certain reference point. For example, if the reference is being fearful, then this pattern will continuously check if you're feeling fearful.

Like a radar, it will look at whether you're more fearful or less fearful. This expectation that you're going to be fearful can then become a self-fulfilling prophecy.

Such thinking can be helpful when done occasionally or for a specific and limited amount of time. Doing so continuously though, is very energy intensive and actually doesn't add anything new or helpful.

Snowballing: *"If this ... then that ... "*

This thought pattern, also known as "catastrophising", only perceives the worst possible outcome. It's like a snowball gathering more and more snow until it triggers an avalanche. For example, thinking *"If I don't answer my friend's text immediately, then they might be upset and not want to be friends with me anymore."*

If the friendship is vulnerable, this could be helpful to remind you to take action to safeguard the friendship. However, if snowballing is your default pattern, it's unlikely to have any bearing on the state of your friendship. In fact, it could leave you feeling resentful for prioritising replying over something more urgent.

To-do list thinking: *"I have to do X, Y, and Z"*

This pattern collects tasks in a mental list and continuously goes over it. For example, you have a pressing work deadline tomorrow and you spend the evening before listing all the things you need to achieve in order to meet it. Then you keep adding to it until it's 2:00 am and you're eating the contents of the fridge. Not helpful.

Practical to-do lists can be helpful. The key is to get the list out of your head by writing it down and checking for priorities. Be specific and remember your time, task, and resource triangulation from Chapter one.

Inner critic: *"I'm not good enough"*

This pattern acts as your risk manager, running a critical commentary on your thoughts, feelings, and behaviour. More often than not, it's not constructive criticism and leaves you deflated and feeling bad about yourself. Being able to critique yourself can be helpful for your personal development. The thing to bear in mind here is that the inner critic tends to generalise what it perceives as your shortcomings. In Chapter nine you will learn more about self-talk, including why self-compassion is vital and how your inner coach can help.

So, now you know about the seven most common thought patterns, aren't you curious to find out which patterns you habitually fall into?

How can you identify your own thought patterns?

Becoming familiar with the type of thought patterns you habitually do, means that you learn to identify your thoughts more easily over time. Building awareness takes time. Often the thinking that you're doing is so habitual and familiar that you don't realise that you're doing it. One way to build this awareness is by keeping a thought diary. We include an activity to help you do this later in this chapter.

Becoming aware of your feelings, alongside building your **A**wareness of your thought patterns, is the first step to practising your First Aid for Feelings **ABC**.

This second step is bringing your **A**wareness to your **B**reath and body. This relates to the focus, posture, and physical sensations of the six components of state you learnt about in Chapter two.

How can you use your **Breath** and body to feel better?

Bringing your **A**wareness to your **B**reath and body is really helpful when you're struggling with feelings — both physical sensations and emotions — or thought patterns. It's helpful because it enables you to focus on the now. In fact, we'd go as far as making the bold claim that your breath is your portal to "now".

Why? Because breathing is always happening in real time. Think about it for a minute. You can't catch up on breath from last week or stock up on breath for next week. When it comes to thinking though, well, chances are that you're thinking about something in the past or in the future. By bringing your awareness to the present, you interrupt your thought pattern.

One way to do this is with a simple deep breath, more about this soon. Before learning about helpful breathing techniques though, it helps to first understand why it's important to notice where your breath lands in your body.

Where does your breath land in your body?

Is it quite high up in your lungs? Is it along your collarbone? Further down in your sternum? Or perhaps even lower, in your stomach?

03 For most people, the most helpful place for your breath to land when you're struggling with unhelpful thoughts or feelings, is, generally, in your stomach. If you have a tight chest though, drawing your breath in your stomach may not be helpful. If this is true for you, just allow your breath to settle where it feels like it wants to. The focus is on trying to soften the breath around wherever it lands.

So, if you're aware that you're beginning to struggle, try to move your breath down to the part of your body where it feels most comfortable for you. If this is your stomach, putting your hands on it helps. You should be able to feel it falling and rising as you breathe in and out.

The 5/7 breathing exercise below (exercise 3.2) is helpful to perform when you're beginning to struggle with feelings. It's one we know to work, and that's very simple to grasp.

Other breathing exercises are available, such as 4x4 or box breathing, pursed lip breathing, and alternate nostril breathing. If you know these, or any others, and have found them helpful already, then stick with them. At the end of the day they are all designed to do the same thing: alter oxygen and carbon dioxide levels in your brain. Doing so can enable you to bring all of your brain back online during a stressful situation. We explain more about the science behind this in Chapter four.

There are other helpful ways you can bring your awareness to your body when you are struggling with your thoughts and feelings. Doing so is important because, when you're in a stressful situation, your focus is most likely around the top of you, in your shoulders and your head. To summarise, bringing your awareness down to the rest of your body enables you to expand the focus of your mind and steady the flow of oxygen to your brain. This helps you to think and see more clearly.

Try tilting your chin up slightly. How does it make you feel? Now, try tilting it down slightly? Feel any different? For many people, simply changing the position of the chin can hugely impact their mood (or state) in the same way as simple micro-changes made by a musician can change the sound they're making. The more you know your instrument, the more beautiful the sound will be.

So, next time you're struggling with thoughts and feelings, try experimenting with straightening your shoulders, wiggling your fingers and toes, and tilting your chin. If you've been standing still, move around or sit down and vice-versa. If you've been sitting down, stand up, or change your posture so that your brain can receive the sensation feedback from your body that something has changed.

Once you've settled your breathing, making your out-breath longer than your in-breath helps you think more clearly. This is because it changes the biochemistry in your brain — literally. You'll learn more about this in Chapter five. You'll find an exercise later on in this chapter to help you practise this technique too.

Using your **B**reath and body to interrupt your thought patterns, naturally brings you to a place where you've opened up enough mental space to think about what to do next. This enables you to make more helpful choices than you might have been doing before, the final part of your First Aid for Feelings **ABC**. This third step — **C**hoice — relates strongly to whether you're focusing your attention on the past, present, or future — the focus component of state that you learned about in chapter two.

How can you create a more helpful Choice to where you want to be?

The third step in your First Aid for Feelings **ABC** is exploring your choices in terms of the situation, relationship, or experience upon which you're focusing. As with "**B**reath and body", "**C**hoice" is so important that we've given it its own chapter. For now, here are some questions to get you started:

- How would I like to think and feel about X?

- What would be more helpful at this moment?

- What one action can I take in the next little while that would make this experience easier?

- If I continue in this way, where does it take me?

Sound implausible? That may be in part because common lingo in many western cultures revolves around the dual approach of positive / negative or good / bad paths. Often, such binary thinking leads you to the roundabout of unhelpful thoughts, rather than onto the road of possibility.

Still sounding tricky? Let's stand on the shoulders of giants then.

Think about Nelson Mandela, who, being imprisoned for 27 years, made the choice to forgive those who imprisoned him. His advice on the matter of choice is, *"May your choices reflect your hopes, not your fears."*

Or Viktor Frankl, the Austrian neurologist / psychiatrist and holocaust survivor whose book, *Man's Search for Meaning*, is among the most influential works of psychiatric literature since Freud. In it, you'll find much wisdom, including the following quote, *"Everything can be taken from a man but one thing: the last of the human freedoms — to choose one's attitude in any given set of circumstances, to choose one's own way."*

Still, in spite of these wise words from inspirational individuals who have made brave choices, we recognise that sometimes considering there is a choice feels radical and even far-fetched.

The invitation here is to get curious about the two different levels of your experience: firstly, how you are thinking and feeling about what is happening; secondly, what is factually happening.

You often have a much greater choice about the first one — how you're thinking and feeling about it — and therefore that is a good place to examine first. Feelings are not facts, they are information, so what is the information your feelings are trying to tell you?

In the beginning this is likely to be confusing and challenging. That is understandable, after all, it's likely that you've been doing your habitual type of thinking for a long time.

When it comes to choosing how to feel, resist the temptation to want to choose something that feels too different to how you are actually feeling in the moment. For example, if you're feeling agitated, then expecting to be able to feel calm is unrealistic. The change in physiology and your biochemistry between these two states is too great to be manageably achieved in one step. It is far more realistic and helpful to choose to feel a bit calmer and then use the learning you have gained about how to create that feeling.

Practice

You've learnt about the philosophy and the science behind the First Aid for Feelings **ABC**. You're now about to start putting it into practice with two simple exercises.

If, to start with, these exercises feel difficult, read Grace's story at the end of this chapter. Grace used these exercises to help her break out of her habit of reference thinking. Have a read, it might help you to see how these exercises could help you too.

Putting your **ABC** into practice may not come easily at first, and this may sound strange, but every time you practise your **ABC**s, you are changing the way your brain works. Gradually over time, with persistent practice, your brain is becoming more flexible and agile.

Exercise 3.1: Your thought journal

For three consecutive days, take 15 minutes at the beginning or end of each day to write down as a stream of consciousness, whatever's going on in your head. By stream of consciousness, we mean, literally, write down exactly what you're thinking as you're thinking it. Don't stop to analyse, don't worry about spelling or grammar, or structure, just let whatever you are thinking flow out through your pen, or your fingers, onto the page.

You can do this in a notebook, on your computer, or on the notes section of your phone, or in a journaling app.

Do not edit it, do not read it after you have written it. Just write down your thoughts for 15 minutes, then stop and leave for at least three days.

Exercise 3.2: Your most common thought patterns

Having taken a break from your thought journal, set aside time and take yourself somewhere nice to read through what you've written. Remember it's more helpful to be curious than critical, so go gently with yourself as you see your thoughts written down.

Reflect upon the thought patterns that you are learning about and note which ones you see in your journal. It's common to see them all, but likely that there are a few which you do more of the time. To help you, here is the list of the most common thought patterns you've learnt about in this chapter:

- Mental tennis *(Should I do this or that?)*
- Reference thinking *(I can't do this because ...)*
- Snowballing *(If this, then that)*
- Ruminating *(If only I ...)*
- Rehearsing *(I am going to ...)*
- To do listing *(I have to do X, Y, Z)*
- Inner critic *(I'm not good enough).*

Exercise 3.3: Your **ABC** Exercise

Take a thought pattern from your thought diary and use it to apply the **ABC** method.

1 **A**wareness: bring to mind one of the experiences associated with this thought pattern. What were you thinking, feeling, and doing during the particular incident you recorded?

2 Bring your awareness to **B**reath and your body.

Put your hands on your stomach, or the area of your body where you feel most comfortable allowing your breath to land. This reminds you to focus on landing your breath in this part of your body.

Take a deep breath in through your nose, counting to five as you do so. If you are focussing on landing your breath in your stomach, you will feel your stomach expand.

Exhale through your mouth, counting to seven as you do so. If you're focussing on your stomach, you will feel it contract and empty.

3 Explore the two levels of your experience. Get curious. What is actually going on, factually? What is your perception of what's going on and how is that affecting you in terms of what you're thinking, feeling, and doing? Use the questions below to help you explore potential choices:

- *If I continue to think this way, where will that take me? What about if I'm still thinking this way in a year's time? 5 years' time? 15 years' time?*

- *What would I like to think about / feel instead of what I'm thinking about / feeling right now?*

- *What would be a more helpful thought / feeling right now?*

- *What one action could I take in the next little while to make this experience easier?*

To help you remember your more helpful **C**hoice, write it down, and come back to it later when you forget. One way we both remember our reminder phrases is to set them as our password for our computers for the week. That way we get to remember them and see them every time we start our computers up. Remember, in sight is in mind!

In the beginning it can be helpful to work through the **ABC** for a specific experience that you've had and would like to have handled differently. This means that you're not putting yourself under pressure to learn how to use it whilst the situation is happening, and you have the benefit of hindsight. Once you've done that a few times you'll develop the confidence to use it for situations that are challenging but not super stressful. As your confidence and ability grows you'll be able to apply it in more and more challenging circumstances. Just like when you're learning to swim, you learn the basic moves whilst still at the side of the pool before beginning to practise in the shallow end. Only once you've built up enough confidence in the shallow end do you venture into deeper waters.

Exercise 3.4: Reflecting on what you've learnt

Now that you've identified your habitual experiences (what you think, feel, and do) what do you notice about:

- What it was like to do these exercises? Was it easy, informative, difficult, confusing?

- Was it easier or more difficult than you expected to identify the thought patterns or to make the actual choices about what to do differently?

- How aware were you before doing these exercises about your thought patterns and the answers you've written down?
- How do you feel about the thoughts and ideas you're having about how you could respond differently to what's going on?

What are you learning about yourself?

I am learning that I ....

....

....

....

....

....

....

....

....

....

....

....

....

Grace's story (She/her)

Grace dreaded spending time with her mum. Whenever she did, she was itching to get away. Her mum had started to try to keep Grace with her for longer: jobs that needed doing; cakes that needed eating. This made Grace dread the visits even more.

Using the **ABC** technique, Grace got curious about what this was about and came to realise the feeling was guilt. Having become **A**ware of this feeling and naming it "guilt", Grace focused on her **B**reath and body to soothe the feelings she was experiencing. These feelings included a racing heart, a dry mouth, and an inability to focus. Once she'd done that it became possible to think more clearly.

Moving on to **C**hoice, she asked herself, *"Is this feeling helpful?"*. The answer was *"Yes"* and *"No"*. *"Yes"*, in that it highlighted to her a belief that she held. This belief was that people should feel guilty towards their parents if they weren't doing everything their parents expected them to do. She also realised that this wasn't really her own belief but a belief that she'd inherited from her mum and other people around her. *"No"*, in that she really didn't want to do the things her mum expected her to do.

She then asked herself, *"What information would I be missing out on if I didn't have this feeling?"*. She realised that the guilt was showing her the belief and that the belief was not helpful. What would be more helpful? Finding a way to be with her mum that they both enjoyed.

The next time she visited her mum, Grace suggested a few things they could do together that they would both enjoy. These included visiting places from their past together and seeing old friends. She also asked her mum what she would enjoy doing. Her mum suggested joining an art group and having a meal out, trialling different restaurants in a nearby town. In this way, they crafted a list of "date" nights to ensure they were doing things together that they both enjoyed. It worked a treat.

03 Summary

In this chapter, you've learnt:

- Why the **ABC** mnemonic (**A**wareness, **B**reath and body, **C**hoice) of First Aid for Feelings is as important as the **ABC** (Airway, Breathing, Circulation) mnemonic of medical first aid

- What the most common thought patterns are for most people

- How to identify your own thought patterns

- How, when you are struggling with feelings or thought patterns, to use your breath and body to take you from where you are now to where you want to be

- How to create helpful choices to take you to where you want to be.

You are now ready to learn about how your brain works, and why it's like a three-scoop ice-cream (yes, really, a three-scoop ice-cream).

Chapter 04

What will you learn?

How two-thirds of everyone's brain operates at
the level of a dog or a cat, and one-third at the
level of a crocodile

Why you sometimes can't access all of your
brain and how this affects your thoughts
and state

Why and how, by changing the way that you
think, you are changing the physical structure
of your brain

Why awareness is important and that without
it you can't change anything

How the **ABC** technique is designed to get you
reconnected to the part of your brain that you
lose when you are struggling.

You've begun to develop your health and
emotional literacy. You've learnt how to use **First
Aid for Feeling's ABC** to help you in emergency
situations relating to your physical sensations and
emotions — yup "feelings".

Now, it's time to delve deeper.

04

Charlie's story (They/them)

Charlie had experienced a very bad day at work. Due to a combination of anxiety-provoking happenings, they were close to losing their temper with the family and depositing the dinner in the bin. Remembering that their brain was like a three-scoop ice-cream, and using the techniques we reveal in this chapter, Charlie saved the day and the dinner. They prevented the situation from spiralling into an ongoing and unnecessary family drama too.

You can read Charlie's full story at the end of this chapter.

Philosophy

Let's start by having a look at what is going on inside your brain when you're experiencing challenging feelings. We'll borrow Professor Linden's helpful metaphor of the brain as a three-scoop ice-cream[14] to help here.[15][16]

How parts of your brain operate like a dog and a crocodile

Your ability to function is affected by a number of factors. These include physical needs, such as whether you are rested enough, and whether you are getting enough energy in your food. It also includes your ability to think clearly. As you learnt in Chapter one, thoughts are one of the components of state.

The state you are in affects how much of your brain is available to you for thinking. Believe it or not, this is because your brain kind of functions like a three-scoop ice-cream. Yes, really. Read on.

It's important to be clear that this analogy is not, as such, anatomically accurate. The metaphor refers to the brain as the three scoops of the ice-cream, with the ice-cream cone being from your neck downwards. It is a helpful way to present and visualise the type of thoughts that are associated with each scoop.

The first scoop

Within the metaphor of the three-scoop ice-cream, the oldest part of the brain is closest to the neck, often referred to as the reptilian part of the brain. That means it's associated with reptiles, like crocodiles. The invitation is to envisage that the thinking that happens in this part of the brain is the kind of thinking you'd imagine a crocodile would do. This includes "all or nothing" thinking, where things are either good or bad and there's no distinction for any other perspective. The focus is on your most primal needs like food, sex, and rest, as well as basic emotions, such as fear and joy. Here there's the quality of an "it's me against them" mindset. When you're stuck here, your choices are seriously limited because you can't see the bigger picture or access your sense of empathy with others.

Crocodiling

Gerund

When you're reacting from the most primal part of your brain, referred to as the reptilian brain (hence crocodile).

At this point, you've not got access to the part of your brain that can access empathy, nor are you able to see and make helpful choices.

Figure 4.2 Crocodiling

The second scoop

This scoop refers to the often-named mammalian part of the brain.[17] The word mammalian refers to the group of animals called mammals, such as horses, and dogs.

A key driver for mammals is to belong to a pack or group. Therefore, this scoop is all about group dynamics, the social structures that ensure your safety within your group. The focus is on more complex emotions like guilt, love, jealousy, and confidence. When you're stuck here, you think in terms of groups, for example, *"It's us against them"*. Your ability to empathise with others is limited to the group that you associate yourself with. You struggle to feel empathy with those who aren't in your group. This mindset of *"It's us against them"* then controls and limits the choices you can perceive.

The third scoop

This scoop refers to what's often described as the rational part of the brain, or the prefrontal cortex. The focus is on observations, analysing situations, separating out different types of thoughts or sensory inputs and assessing them. When you're able to access this level of thinking, you can solve complex problems. You can think through sequences and outcomes, like working out a travel itinerary. Here, you can see the bigger picture and the mindset is one of *"We're all in this together".*

With access to the bigger picture and the ability to empathise with others, not just those in your group, you are able to see choices and potential. Such choices would be unavailable to you without access to your top scoop (more on this later).

Top scoop:
"we're in this together"

Group scoop:
"it's us and them"

Crocodile scoop:
"me versus everyone else"

Figure 4.3 Three-scoop ice-cream with thought examples

When all three scoops are available to you, it's like they're all online and the Wi-Fi is strong and sturdy. You are connected to yourself and others. However, there are days, or moments within days, when that's not the case at all. When the connection drops you lose access to your top scoop and, if the connection drops further, you also lose your group scoop, leaving you with only your crocodile scoop.

If this resonates, know you're not alone. It's a human thing, not a personality trait. That means it's not because you are you, it's because you are human. We all do it. All of us. Which is why, in these moments of struggling, you can be kind to yourself.

Being kind to yourself means practising your **ABC**: Become **A**ware of when you're crocodiling by recognising the indicators. Use your **B**reath and body to bring you into real-time and get the rest of your brain back online. Ask yourself what you're thinking, feeling, and doing, and whether it's helpful. Then ask yourself what might be a more helpful **C**hoice to do instead.

This "being kind to yourself" may sound a little alien, or even a little too "hippy dippy" for you. It's not. In fact, a rapidly growing body of scientific research[18] shows how kindness has a direct and fundamental impact on your health.[19]

Why you sometimes can't access all of your brain and how this affects you

Earlier we talked about how your ability to use all your scoops to think can be obscured. Well, the thing doing the "obscuring" is stress.[20] Let's take a closer look.

Your state is more complicated than it appears at first sight. So much goes into making it what it is. Indeed, your state is not just an expression of your physical sensations and emotions. Remember the six components of state concept you learnt about in Chapter one? This concept explains how your state is the result of a combination of thoughts, emotions, voice, focus, posture, and sensations.

Interconnected with the six components of state, there is also the matter of your pre-programmed fight-or-flight-or-freeze response to take into consideration, commonly referred to as the "stress state". As any book you read about stress will advise, the stress state is a survival mechanism which we all have. It kicks in automatically when your brain detects something it perceives as a threat. Now anything can be perceived as a threat, whether that's something physical, mental, or social.

The purpose of the stress state is to prepare you to fight for survival, run away (flight), or freeze — depending on what's considered to be the most successful action to take. In order to achieve this, your internal resources, like energy, power, and focus, are organised and optimised to secure your survival.

The brain is your most energy-intensive organ, using up 20 percent of all your available energy.[21] It therefore makes sense that resources are diverted away from your brain towards the systems you need most at this point.[22] After all, it's better to use the energy to run from or fight a threat like a tiger than spend it wondering whether the tiger has had breakfast.

You'll learn more about what happens to your body's other priorities, like digestion and healing, when you're in a stress state, in the next chapter.

What is happening in your brain when fight-or-flight-or-freeze response is on?

When you face a threat, say, an oncoming car, your eyes or ears (or both) send the information to your amygdala. This is the area of the brain that contributes to emotional processing and detecting threats. The amygdala interprets the images and sounds. When it perceives a threat, it instantly sends a distress signal to your hypothalamus, the part of your brain which acts as a command centre. The hypothalamus, in turn, signals to the rest of your body, telling it to get ready to fight or run (flee). If neither option feels viable, you will freeze, like a possum.

These physical changes happen so quickly that it's likely you're not aware of them until after they've come into effect. In fact, your wiring is so efficient that the amygdala and hypothalamus start this reaction even before the brain's visual centres have had a chance to fully process what is happening. That's why people are able to jump out of the path of an oncoming car even before they think about what they're doing.

Once the danger is over, your systems return to your habitual state again. This means your body's able to look after everyday maintenance and well-being. If your stress state is triggered too frequently, this ability to move between stress and maintenance is affected. This can have serious physical, mental, and even social consequences. More about the physical mechanics of this in Chapter five. For now, let's focus on what you can do about it.

04 Why changing your thinking changes your brain

Being able to adjust and support your state is a vital skill. Understanding how you can experiment with the six components of state means you can affect and change your state. Because state is interconnected with your feelings and behaviour, these change too.

In this chapter we're focusing on thoughts but you can apply this to any or each of the six components. Over the last century, there's been a growing body of evidence showing that working with your thoughts can actually change the physical structure of your brain. This ability is called neuroplasticity. The word was coined by Jerzy Konorski in 1948[23] and Marian Diamond[24] trail-blazed a lot of the research that helped us understand it better.

Neuroplasticity refers to the ability you have to develop and affect the way your brain works. Scientists used to think that our brains developed during childhood and that, once we became adults, they stopped changing. However, modern brain-scanning technology has established that this isn't so. In fact, our brain's cells (neurons) continue to change throughout our lives, both structurally (non-synaptic plasticity) and in the way they connect and work together (synaptic plasticity). This can be seen most profoundly with people who have suffered a stroke where a part of the brain has been damaged. Rehabilitation and treatment has, in many cases, enabled them to regain abilities and function by training the brain to build new ways of working.

Taxi drivers' brains grow to navigate London's streets

Need further evidence of neuroplasticity? Neuroscientists[25] compared magnetic resonance imaging (MRI) scans of new London cab drivers to those of new New York cab drivers over a four-year period.

At the start of the study, all participants had more or less the same size hippocampus (the part of the brain responsible for spatial awareness). By the end, London cab drivers not only had larger hippocampus than New York cabbies, they consistently scored higher in memory tests too.

What may have caused such differences? Learning how to get around London streets is far more complex than learning how to get around in New York. This is because New York is based on an easy-to-navigate grid system. The conclusion was that, by memorising London's streets, the city's cabbies had literally built more neural pathways. This showcases neuroplasticity in action and that you can train yourself to learn and think in new ways. And it isn't just about thoughts and feelings, it's also about the thoughts and feelings that you have about your thoughts and feelings.

The thing about thoughts and feelings ...

You see, the thing about thoughts and feelings is that you have thoughts and feelings about the thoughts and feelings you are having. And, guess what? It's almost always more helpful to address these thoughts and feelings about the thoughts and feelings we have, before addressing the core thoughts and feelings.

For example, you can have anxious thoughts about feeling in pain, and you can feel sad that you're feeling angry. We all do it and it's perfectly OK. Addressing the anxious and sad feelings first will clear the way to the pain and anger feelings. The thoughts and feelings are clues, there to give you valuable information about what you need to address to help you support or shift your state. When you can do this, you're better able to respond to what's going on in a more helpful way.

Now, this may sound difficult or even fanciful. It's not, but, like most things in life, it takes practise. You cannot learn to support or shift your state by just reading the manual. Reading it is the first step though, so, do please read on!

You'll learn more in Chapter five about supporting or shifting your state by coming to your **B**reath and body and then making more helpful choices. For now, let's first get curious about how this technique is designed to get back the part of your brain that you lose when your primitive fight-or-flight-or-freeze response is triggered.

How the **ABC** technique helps you get your brain back

When you are feeling under pressure — be that physical, mental, or social — it's vital that you recognise the indicators. This is why our **ABC** technique begins with "awareness".

Being unaware of the indicators around you, being on autopilot, is like being on a physical journey and not noticing the signs that you're heading in the wrong direction. We've all started off heading somewhere, only to end up somewhere else because we've stopped focussing and gone into autopilot mode. Thor, for example, would sometimes do this, ending up at the supermarket, rather than the train station. This was simply because the two locations were near to each other, and Thor went more often to the supermarket than the train station, so that was the default mode.

Similarly, if you're on autopilot, getting through your day, unaware of the indicators that your body and mind are giving you about potential threats, you simply won't realise in time. Even the cleverest person in the world will not be able to change direction in time if they do not know they are heading in the wrong direction.

The focus on **A**wareness is not exclusive to First Aid for Feelings. Every mindfulness practice, school of Buddhism, and school of psychology starts with **A**wareness training. Think about it: if you don't feel the pain or see blood, you won't know that you need to bandage or plaster a cut. This applies to all thoughts and feelings.

Once you're **A**ware of your thoughts and feelings, you're able to do something about them. This is why getting curious about your indicators (which you learnt about in Chapter two) is so important. **A**wareness is something that strengthens with practice and becomes easier.

The next step is to bring your focus to your **B**reath and body — the **B** in First Aid for Feelings' **ABC**. This helps you to either keep or bring back online, the part of your brain that you lose access to when your fight-or-flight-or-freeze response is triggered.

This works because it helps you bring your focus to real-time. Remember what you learnt in Chapter three? Your breath is always in real-time. Whilst your thoughts can be all over the place, your breath only exists in real-time. You can't store your breath for next week. Indeed, your breath is there to serve you in the moment and, once you grasp this, you can use it to help your body change gear, almost as you would use a gearbox in a car. We'll show you how in Chapter five.

You've learnt a metaphor for how your brain works and how this means that you can be kinder to yourself when you're struggling. Being kinder to yourself simply means recognising that, when you think, feel, or do things that you later regret, it is not absolutely down to you. It is a human trait that we all do from time to time. When you have less access to your brain, your ability to make skillful and helpful choices is limited.

Take heart from the fact that how your brain works is not cast in iron, but rather something to be developed and strengthened. You can, with practice, change the way you think and feel.

As you progress through this manual, you will become more and more skilled in using the **ABC** technique and other components of your First Aid for Feelings. In the final chapter, we will guide you to create your own First Aid for Feelings Kit. First though, it's time to put some of your new learning into practice and strengthen your **A**wareness.

04 Practice

As always when getting practical, remember to be as gentle with yourself and kind as you're able to be. Ready to start practising using the **ABC** technique to bring back the part of your brain that you lose when you're under pressure?

Let's go.

Exercise 4.1: How do you know you're crocodiling?

Identify three to five thoughts, feelings, or behaviours that let you know that you're crocodiling.

1 ....

2 ....

3 ....

4 ....

5 ....

Exercise 4.2: What can you now do that took effort to learn?

Name three activities or skills that you now do effortlessly but were challenging for you to learn in the first place. This could be, for example, driving, cooking a Sunday roast, or learning how to use a new app on your phone.

Then ask yourself why you bothered sticking with each activity or skill, and how it has helped you since you've learnt it.

First example	
Main challenge	
Why bother	
Benefit	

Second example	
Main challenge	
Why bother	
Benefit	

Third example	
Main challenge	
Why bother	
Benefit	

Figure 4.4 Effortful to effortless

Exercise 4.3: Identifying which scoop is driving your thoughts and feelings

Choose three situations where you struggled with your thoughts and feelings. These could be the situations you identified in Chapter two, or other situations or experiences. Thinking back to your thoughts at the time, which scoop of the brain do you think they came from?

Here's a recap:

- Top scoop - *"we're all in this together"*

- Group scoop - *"it's us versus them"*

- Crocodile scoop - *"it's me versus everyone else"*

First experience	
Key thoughts	
Scoop	

Second experience	
Key thoughts	
Scoop	

Third experience	
Key thoughts	
Scoop	

Figure 4.5 What scoop is driving thoughts and feelings

Exercise 4.4: Reflecting on what you've learnt

Now that you've insight into how your brain works and what it's capable of, what do you notice about:

· What it was like to do these exercises? Was it, for example, easy, informative, difficult, or confusing?

· Your ability to learn new skills. Do you take it for granted? Do you dismiss how hard it was to learn something that's now easy?

· How the way your brain works when you're struggling has affected your ability to be skillful?

· Thoughts and ideas you're having about how you could respond differently?

What are you learning about yourself?

I am learning that I ....

....

....

....

....

....

....

....

....

04 Charlie's story (They/them)

Charlie returned home from a bad day at the office to take a frustrating call from mum. Their back was hurting. Combined with the feeling that they were doing everything in the family home and their partner and children were just cruising, Charlie was seriously fed up.

Unpacking the dishwasher whilst letting the dogs out, stepping over piles of washing, and calling the family down for the tea they'd just cooked, Charlie dropped and smashed a plate. Remembering their First Aid for Feelings, they quickly became **A**ware of indicators that they were fed up: racing heart, quickened breathing, prickles up the back of their neck.

They immediately stood up and stepped away from the dishwasher and broken plate. Bringing their attention to their **B**reath and body, Charlie breathed in to the count of five and out to the count of seven. Repeating this three times, they had calmed down enough to ask: *"What am I thinking, feeling, and doing?"*.

The answer was *"I'm thinking I'm going to lose it. Why do I always have to do everything? I'm feeling fed up and angry. I'm crocodiling and speeding up."* Thanks to using the **A** and **B** of First Aid for Feelings' **ABC** — they changed their posture and brought their focus to the present. Feeling more resourceful, they were then able to make a more helpful **C**hoice.

Instead of doing the usual and yelling at their family, Charlie asked themself what could be more helpful. They realised the answer was to slow down and remember that it wasn't all down to them. They didn't need to do everything, they could ask for help. So, that's what they did.

Everybody was happy to help. Their partner quickly cleared up the broken plate, the youngest child let the dogs in, and the older child put the clothes into the washing machine. Then they all sat down to eat dinner together. The food was still warm and they all felt that they'd contributed to changing what could have been a stressful situation into something that connected them all together.

Summary

In this chapter, you have learnt:

- How, metaphorically, two-thirds of everyone's brain operates at the level of a dog or a cat, and one-third at the level of a crocodile

- Why you sometimes can't access all of your brain and how this affects your thoughts and state

- Why and how, by changing the way that you think, you're changing the physical structure of your brain

- Why **A**wareness is important and that without it you can't change anything

- How the **ABC** technique is designed to get you reconnected to the part of your brain that you lose when you're struggling.

You're now ready to learn how breathing mindfully helps to release stress and improves your ability to think more clearly.

Chapter 05

What will you learn?

How breathing mindfully helps to release stress and improves your ability to think more clearly

How the **ABC** technique helps you move more effortlessly between the stress and maintenance states

Why breathing isn't just what you've been doing since you were born and how, with practise, you can use breathing techniques to shift from the stress to the maintenance state.

Why the fact that your breath is always operating in real-time is helpful

How, by staying in real-time, rather than spiralling into the future or the past, you are able to create the space to find more choices.

Winston's story (He/him)

When Winston met a new client, he was unexpectedly taken aback by a sudden sense of fear. **A**ware that he was tipping into the stress state, he used the **B**reath and body exercises you are about to learn in this chapter. This enabled him to bring himself into the maintenance state, where he was able to understand why this was happening and reconnect with his confidence. You can read Winston's full story at the end of this chapter.

05 Philosophy

You've now learnt how the stress state directly affects your ability to think. When it ramps up, your ability to think goes down. This is a key insight to add to your **A**wareness of what goes on for you when you struggle. Given how essential this state is to your survival and the impact it has on your ability to function, it's important to learn how to channel it and work with it. So far the focus has been on strengthening the A, that is, the **A**wareness component of the **ABC** technique, let's move on to the **B** — **B**reath and body.

In this chapter we look more deeply into the science of how your **B**reath and body help you to do that. Before coming to the body, we begin by looking into how breathing mindfully helps to release stress, thereby improving your ability to think more clearly. You'll learn why your breath is the gateway to choice, or, as James Nestor describes it in his book *Breath, the New Science of a Lost Art*, a power switch.[26]

How breathing mindfully eases stress and improves your thinking

As you learnt in the previous chapter, all of us come with an in-built protection and survival mechanism, a fight-or-flight-or-freeze response — or stress state. This state is triggered by the part of your brain called the amygdala, which acts like your sentinel, always on the lookout for potential threats.

Once a threat is sensed, the amygdala sends a message to the hypothalamus, the part of your brain that acts kind of like your "headquarters" or HQ. This sets off a chain reaction throughout your body getting you ready to respond so that you survive the threat.

This chain reaction is all about the focus of your Autonomic Nervous System, often referred to as ANS for short. Both the stress state and the maintenance state belong to the ANS.[27] If you like technical jargon, then the technical name for the stress state is the Sympathetic Nervous System (SNS), and for the maintenance state, the Parasympathetic Nervous System (PNS).

Imagine the ANS as the manager responsible for allocating resources, like your energy and focus, as effectively and efficiently as possible. When everything is tootling along quite nicely, your maintenance state is using up most of your energy budget. Here, there's a sense of not just the present, but also the future. When the chain reaction of responding to a threat starts, your ANS redistributes your resources to the systems and organs that are designed to respond quickly. Here it's all about being able to fight for your survival or run to safety. It's about the present moment only, because, unless you survive now, there's no future.

A helpful metaphor here is to think of the ANS as having a mixing desk like sound engineers do. The desk has sliders (called "level control faders") that can be moved up or down for each system or state depending on what's needed and most helpful at any given time.

Everyone spends some of the day in the stress state and some in the maintenance state. This is healthy. When you're in the maintenance state, all three scoops of your brain are online and available. You're able to choose how to respond to what happens to you, once you've become aware of what's going on.

When you are in the stress state, particularly when it's intense, your level of thinking is on par with that of a crocodile. You're likely to snap and your thinking is likely to be reactive and instinctual, characterised by either / or choices and snowballing. Just to refresh your memory, snowballing is when you start with a single thought that then gathers more and more snow until it becomes like an avalanche.

And, if you spend too much time in the stress state, you tip out of healthy, helpful stress into unhealthy, unhelpful stress. The sort where you can become stuck and ill.

Here's a brief overview of what happens in your body when you're in the stress state and when you're in the maintenance state:

The Stress State

The Maintenance State

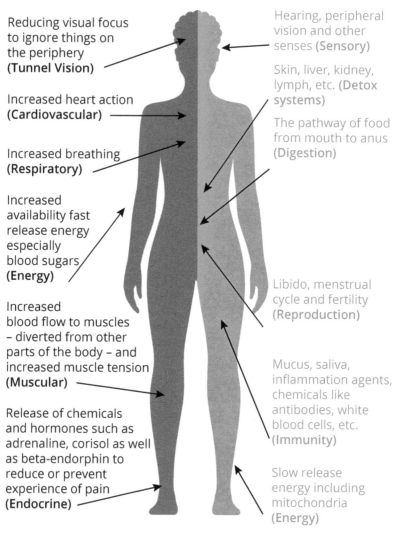

Reducing visual focus to ignore things on the periphery **(Tunnel Vision)**

Increased heart action **(Cardiovascular)**

Increased breathing **(Respiratory)**

Increased availability fast release energy especially blood sugars **(Energy)**

Increased blood flow to muscles – diverted from other parts of the body – and increased muscle tension **(Muscular)**

Release of chemicals and hormones such as adrenaline, corisol as well as beta-endorphin to reduce or prevent experience of pain **(Endocrine)**

Hearing, peripheral vision and other senses **(Sensory)**

Skin, liver, kidney, lymph, etc. **(Detox systems)**

The pathway of food from mouth to anus **(Digestion)**

Libido, menstrual cycle and fertility **(Reproduction)**

Mucus, saliva, inflammation agents, chemicals like antibodies, white blood cells, etc. **(Immunity)**

Slow release energy including mitochondria **(Energy)**

Figure 5.1 Stress and Maintenance states

The Maintenance state

When there is no physical, mental, or social threat in sight, you're in the maintenance state. Your parasympathetic nervous system is fully resourced so that you can get on with the business of living: eating, sleeping, detoxing, and creating.

All of the body's systems run automatically. You have a healthy balance of hormones and a plentiful energy store from which to draw. Hence this state is often referred to as the "rest and repair", or "rest and digest".

A healthy body knows how to do this in a proportional and healthy way. As mentioned earlier, the ANS acts like a manager and sound engineer, dialling up and down your states to keep you safe and well. However, the body can be pushed beyond its limits into unhelpful stages of stress. This can be, for example, if you're constantly feeling under pressure from yourself, others, or external factors, such as heightened and persistent threats. We describe these stages later in this chapter.

The Stress state

Remember when you see or hear something that your brain interprets as a threat, say a fire, your amygdala notifies your hypothalamus. Your hypothalamus gets your ANS involved directing resources to your stress state and away from your maintenance state.

But what does that actually mean? It means releasing hormones, such as adrenaline and cortisol into the bloodstream, which sets off a multitude of physical changes. Here is a list of some of the main ones:

- **Eyes**: your visual focus tunes out everything on the periphery. You get tunnel vision

- **Heart**: your heart begins to beat faster and harder to pump blood containing oxygen and sugar to your major muscles to use for energy. You may feel your heart beating as you breathe more rapidly

- **Lungs**: your breathing rate increases and your airways dilate. More oxygen enters your blood

- **Brain**: your mental activity and alertness increase for quick decision-making. This change is quick and temporary as the human body is not able to hold such hyper-focus for long

- **Blood**: blood flow to your muscles increases to prepare you for action, either fight or flight. The blood thickens to increase the availability of clotting factors and immune system cells in case of an injury

- **Legs and arms**: sugars and fats are converted for use as energy and sent to your major muscles to help you to fight or run away

- **Skin and sweat glands**: sweating increases. Hands and feet often feel cold as blood supplies are diverted to your brain and muscles. Hairs stand on end as you experience goose pimples. Skin can turn pale

- **Salivary glands**: there is a decreased flow of saliva. Your mouth can feel dry

- **Gut muscles**: gut activity slows as blood supply is reduced. This can affect digestion and cause digestion issues

- **Spleen**: contracts and empties red blood cells into the circulation to increase oxygen levels

- **Kidneys**: reduces urine formation so that your body can use all of its energy to prepare you to fight or run away

- **Liver and fat tissue**: glucose and fats are mobilised for energy to fuel your muscles.

As your survival is the primary purpose of the stress response, it's undoubtedly helpful. This type of stress is referred to as acute and we'll explain this in more detail later in this chapter.

It's not just about survival though. The stress state is also helpful for building skills, strength, and stamina, all of which can move you beyond your comfort zone. Whether that's learning to drive, climbing a mountain, or competing in sports, utilising the power of the stress state can be incredibly satisfying and important to your health and well-being. Kelly McGonical gave a seminal TED talk on this in 2013 where she talked about the importance of making stress your friend.[28]

The point here's not whether stress is good or bad but whether it's helpful in the moment.

It's worth noting too that there are elements of the stress state that, for a while, can feel good. Indeed, the adrenaline rush and that burst of energy that helps you go the metaphorical extra mile can become addictive. You can begin to unwittingly seek stress just to keep your body adrenalised.

Keeping your body adrenalised, though, is energy intensive and brings with it physical costs. One way to think about where you get that energy from and how you pay for that cost is to imagine it as a personal overdraft facility. It can sometimes be helpful to deal with situations that cost you more than you've got in your account and borrowing from your overdraft allowance makes sense. However, if you continuously live off your overdraft, the interest will eventually become buckling. So much so, that, if you spend too long in the stress state, it progresses from acute to chronic, and eventually to allostatic.

The three stages of stress

Acute stress: The body's survival system, aka stress state, is activated when feeling under threat. This could be when you've a work deadline you need to meet, or when you run out of a burning building, for example. Acute stress is helpful and healthy. "Acute" means that it is a "short term" experience for the body. Once the threat has been dealt with or avoided, the body returns to the maintenance state focussing on the general running of the body's function and systems.

Chronic stress: This is when the body is frequently, and over a sustained period of time, in the stress state. Your body's ability to focus on maintenance and the general running of functions and systems is reduced. Over time, this leads to functions and systems starting to struggle.

Allostatic stress: Also referred to as "allostatic overload",[29] or maladaptive stress. Allostatic stress is when the body has got "stuck" in the state of stress. This means that the body's baseline state is now the stress state, rather than the maintenance state. Even when you create the conditions for your body to focus on maintenance and general running of the body's function and systems, the effect is temporary. The body soon returns to the unhealthy baseline of allostatic stress.

The good news is that we now have a greater understanding of what can be done to address stress and help the body move more effortlessly between the stress and maintenance states. First Aid for Feelings is one of the methods you can use to support yourself back into the maintenance state, with our **ABC** technique coming in really handy.

How does the ABC technique help you move between the stress and maintenance states?

As you learnt in Chapter three, everything begins with **A**wareness (the **A** of our **ABC**), recognising your indicators, using charts, and making maps of when you are feeling stressed.

Once you're aware that you're entering into unhelpful stress you can use your **B**reath and body to bring you back to the present moment, to real-time. As you're about to learn, breathing techniques, like slowing down your breath to less than 10 breaths a minute[30] and doing longer "out" than "in" breaths, help regulate your state.

Why does using longer "out" breaths than "in" breaths help you regulate your state?

Breathing is central to life. Here's how it works:[31]

Breathing is essentially about gas exchange. We breathe in one gas, oxygen, and then breathe out another gas, carbon dioxide, using one of the body's largest organs, the lungs.

When you breathe, oxygen enters the lungs and diffuses[32] into the blood. It's taken to the heart and pumped into the body's cells. At the same time, the carbon dioxide waste from the breakdown of sugars in the cells of the body diffuses into the blood. From here it moves into the lungs and is expelled as we breathe out.

This exchange of gases takes place both in your lungs (external respiration) and in your cells (internal respiration).

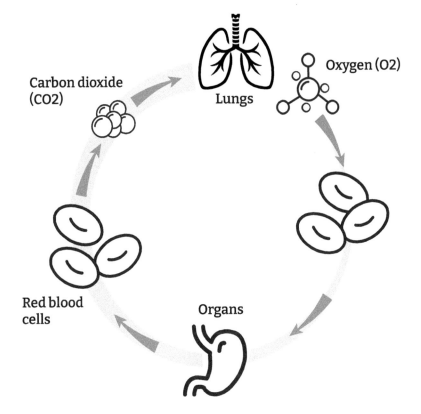

Figure 5.2 Gas exchange in humans

When you're in the stress state, you breathe faster in order to bring in more oxygen so that it can be converted into energy. It goes to functions and systems in your body that help you survive, like the big muscle groups in your thighs that help you run or stand your ground. But, by increasing oxygen, you also increase carbon dioxide.

When you slow down your breath or change the ratio between your in-breath and your out-breath, you alter the biochemistry of your body, including your brain. You help yourself to return your body to the maintenance state. This is why well-being experts are increasingly placing so much emphasis on working with your breath. It's why so many athletes, singers, actors, and public speakers learn to work with their breath too.

05 There are other ways of affecting your biochemistry of course: alcohol, sugar, sex, recreational drugs, non-recreational drugs, etc. You may have used some or all of these at some point in your life in an attempt to get yourself out of the stress state. Most would agree that these ways are not helpful.

There are also other ways of affecting your brain's biochemistry that people commonly perceive as being helpful, but that can become unhelpful, such as the gym, sex, cleaning, or shopping. We all have beliefs about these things, for example, "going to the gym is a good thing" but that may not always be the case.

Ultimately, it comes down to one of Thor's Helpful mantras, "It's not what you do, it's the way that you do it and that's what gets results."[33] Our advice to you here is that, if you're doing any of these activities excessively, especially if doing them feels stressful, to get curious and check: Is it helpful?

All these examples are about feeling better, or at least feeling different. Whatever it is that you do, you're doing in an effort to shift the biochemistry of your brain and body. However, the shift can often feel short-lived and ineffective, even contributing to you feeling worse or dealing with unintended consequences of the choices you've made.

We've all done it, reaching for something to help shift a feeling without thinking it through, or reaching for something that used to be helpful but isn't helpful anymore.

This is where the breath functions as such a powerful aid. It is always in real-time, and because of how it helps your thinking, it acts as your gateway to being able to think through the most helpful choice.

With the **A**wareness that you're struggling, the next step is to come to your breath.

How can you use breathing techniques to shift yourself from the stress to the maintenance state?

Many top athletes and other performers in high-pressure environments use breathing techniques. They do this to help them stay in the more resourceful maintenance state, as well as channelling the power of the stress state to deliver peak performance when required. They know it's their ticket to more brain and body power. But how so? Surely, breathing is just automatic, right?

Not quite. It's true that breathing is something you do automatically. It happens whether you're aware of it or not. However, it's also something you can deliberately affect. When you do become aware of it and learn how to use it, you can get so much more value from it.

Using the metaphor of cars and getting into the driving seat, learning to use your breath means you can help your body and brain change those metaphorical gears. You can move smoothly from the effort involved in the stress state to deliver power and energy, to the effortlessness of the maintenance state where it's business as usual.

An integral part to helpful breathing is breathing in through your nose and out through your mouth. You've probably heard that a million times, but why?

Why is it important to breathe in through your nose and out through your mouth?

Well, in essence, it's because your nose is designed to work as a filtration system. It filters out undesirable particles that would otherwise enter your throat if you were to breathe in through your mouth. It warms air up to body temperature before it gets to your lungs, which is helpful, especially if you have asthma. It also moistens the air as it moves down to your lungs, which eases the gas exchange we mentioned earlier.

Keeping in mind the "In through nose, out through mouth" focus, let's introduce two classic breathing techniques. If you feel like experimenting, do breathe along. If you're not sure, don't worry, you can pick this up in the practise section further on in this chapter.

The 5/7 breathing technique

This technique is all about making the out-breath longer than the in-breath. There are various versions of this technique, for example, 7/11 breathing. You can experiment with a rhythm that feels comfortable to you.

Here's how you do it:

· Breathe in to the count of five through your nose

· Breathe out to the count of seven through your mouth

· Take a moment to give your lungs time to make any adjustments if needed

· Repeat two more times, remembering to give yourself breathing space in between.

The 4 x 4 breathing technique

This technique is also referred to as box breathing because you're creating the shape of a box with your breath. We prefer to call it 4 x 4 breathing because it sits so nicely with our driving-seat and gear-changing analogy. After all, 4 x 4 vehicles are designed for off-road use and you get much more juice from them than regular 2 x 4 vehicles. Once you're familiar with it, you can experiment with increasing the numbers to increase your capacity.

Here's how you do it:

· Breathe in to the count of four

· Hold for the count of four

· Breathe out to the count of four

· Hold for the count of four

· Take a moment to give your lungs time to make any adjustments if needed

· Repeat three more times, remembering to give yourself breathing space in between.

You may have noticed that in 4 x 4 breathing you're not making the out-breath longer than the in-breath. So, you're probably wondering how it shifts you back into the maintenance state. It works by giving your lungs a bit of a workout, making them function outside of their normal rhythm. This disrupts the stress state and supports you into the maintenance state.

Further on in this chapter, we include step-by-step instructions for both breathing exercises. We encourage you to trial each of them over a period of three days. For both techniques allow yourself a short break in between each repetition. During this break just breathe however feels natural. To keep things simple, we recommend repeating the 5 x 7 exercise three times, think 3 x 5 x 7, and the 4 x 4 exercise at least four times, think 4 x 4 x 4. Once you've got a feel for each technique, keep on practising the one you prefer, or, if you like them both, mix and match.

Our intention here is to keep it as simple, memorable, and practical as possible.

Do bear in mind that there are other breathing techniques, such as the alternate nostril breathing often taught in yoga and Buteyko,[34] which has a range of techniques. If you are curious about such techniques and want to take your breathing to the next level, do look into them.

Why is the fact that our breath is always operating in real-time helpful?

Think about it. So long as you are alive, you are breathing, and your breath is with you, always. You can't save it, bottle it up, and keep it for next week. But you can use it to help you use the stress and maintenance states in the most helpful way for you at any given time. Here we're focussing on when it's unhelpful.

Sure, going for a run, bingeing on sugar, or whatever your "go-to" intervention is, could be a bigger hitting intervention than working with your breath in the short term. And, in some specific circumstances, it might genuinely be the most helpful response. Actually learning how to tweak and tilt yourself out of the stress state and into the maintenance state though, makes doing so much more effortless. It's also far more accessible too: after all, you've always got your breath with you. You can use it there and then, rather than wait until you can get out for that run, get that sugar high, or to whatever your "go-to" intervention is.

Stress mainly exists in the past or the future, even if that past was just a few minutes ago, or the future in the next couple of minutes. If the cause of your stress is happening in real-time, and it's truly a threat, then it absolutely is appropriate for you to be in the stress state. We propose that, even in those situations, using your breath to channel the power of this state more effectively is likely to stand you in better stead. However, most of the time, it's unlikely that you're facing an actual threat in real-time. Rather, it's likely that, in fact, at this moment, at this particular point in time, you're OK, or at least OK enough. So let's focus on that.

Have you ever had a deadline that you've needed to meet within, say, the next three hours, that you estimated would require 10 hours of work? Felt stressful, and real-time stressful, didn't it? But, in truth, it wasn't.

This is because the real-time stress point in this situation existed in the future, three hours in the future to be precise. You had time to work out how to keep all three scoops of your brain online, which, let's face it, could have really helped with this situation.

How, by staying in real-time, you're able to create the space to find more choices

The first step is becoming **A**ware that you're entering the stress state, that you're feeling the ramping up of adrenaline in your body. As you learnt in Chapters one and two, this means knowing how feelings, such as stress, show up for you. Being **A**ware so you can then use your **B**reath and body to affect the oxygen to carbon dioxide ratio that's likely to be hijacking your top scoop. Having kept your top scoop online, you can make some **C**hoices about how to manage the stressful situation using the tasks, time, resources triangle you learnt about in Chapter one. Can you negotiate the size of the task, the deadline, or bring in other people or resources to support you? Doing so will help you to keep all scoops online. The deadline will still exist, but you will not be stressed and you will have all of your brain present to help you meet the reshaped challenge. You will be OK, or OK enough.

Being OK enough doesn't necessarily mean we're comfortable, because we can be OK enough and still feel distress, or anger, or discomfort. The key differentiating factor here is to shift from focussing on the unhelpful stress-related feelings to focussing on the most helpful way to address what's going to work with what's happening in real-time, right now. Because the **B**reath and body only exist in real-time, this is your quickest way to move from that past or future into the here and now, into real-time. Not only that, it can keep you here for long enough to allow your top scoop to reconnect. This is the part of your brain you need to help you make more helpful **C**hoices about what action to take next.

> To summarise, think of your breath as your gearbox. If you're driving at 70 miles per hour (mph) in your head and you're stressed, it's like driving at 70 mph in third gear: your engine needs to work really hard.

Whereas, when you're able to work with and channel your breath, it's like going up the gears. Suddenly you're driving at 70 mph but in fifth gear where the engine is not working as hard, and it's more effortless. Experimenting with and getting the feel for different ways of using your breath will give you a better idea as to why and how this makes such a difference.

Moving your focus from your breath to your body

Remember the "posture" and "physical sensations" components of state that we talked about in Chapter one? Your posture has been proven to directly affect the stress state.[35] Adjusting your posture, alongside working with your breath, will therefore make it even more powerful. If you're able to, tracing your fingers along your eyebrows and then along your jawline helps to bring your focus down from the top of your head to the rest of your body below.

Shuffling your shoulders and stance, or, if you're sitting down, your bum, gives you sensory feedback from your body, which increases your experience of what being here feels like. The sensory feedback that travels the furthest distance to your brain is the one from your toes, so give them a wiggle. Even bringing warmth to your body, like with a hot water bottle, can help soothe and ease the stress state[36] and climbing stairs can lower your blood pressure.[37]

05 Practice

The following exercises are designed to help you identify when you are in the stress state and the maintenance state, and to use your breath and body to move consciously between these two states.

As ever, please keep in mind the helpful mantra that it is "always more helpful to be curious than critical".

Exercise 5.1: Identifying indicators for the stress and maintenance states

Name three to five indicators that let you know that you're in the maintenance state.

....

....

....

....

....

....

....

....

....

Name three to five indicators that let you know that you're in the stress state.

....

....

....

....

....

....

....

....

Exercise 5.2: Experimenting with your breathing

1   Practise the 5/7 breathing technique. Here's a reminder of how it works:

    ·   Breathe in to the count of five through your nose

    ·   Breathe out to the count of seven through your mouth

    ·   Take a moment to give your lungs time to make any adjustments, if needed

    ·   Repeat two more times, remembering to give yourself breathing space in between.

2   Practise the 4 x 4 breathing technique. Here's a reminder of how it works:

- Breathe in to the count of four
- Hold for the count of four
- Breathe out to the count of four
- Hold for the count of four
- Take a moment to give your lungs time to make any adjustments, if needed
- Repeat three more times, remembering to give yourself breathing space in between.

3 What do you notice about each technique?

4 What's different in terms of how you experience each technique?

Exercise 5.3: Experimenting with using your body to change your breath and your state

Remember the six components of state from Chapter one? Posture, physical sensations, and tone of voice are all related to your body Experiment doing something with your body, like walking up and down the stairs, sitting down if you've been standing up, or the other way around. Or even just shuffle your shoulders and change your posture.

- What happens with your breath?
- What happens with your body?

Exercise 5.4: Reflecting on what you've learnt

Now you've learnt about breathing, and the stress and maintenance states, what do you notice about:

- What it was like to do these exercises? Was it, for example, easy, informative, difficult, or confusing?
- Your ability to learn new skills. Do you take it for granted? Do you dismiss how hard it was to learn something that's now easy?
- Thoughts and ideas you're having about how you could respond differently in the future?

What are you learning about yourself?

I am learning that I ....

....

....

....

....

....

....

....

....

....

....

....

....

....

....

05 Winston's story (He/him)

Winston was going into a meeting with a new client who he'd only ever spoken to on the phone. When they met in person, Winston became aware of his indicators for stress and fear, which included a racing heart, a tingly scalp, and a sense that everything was too loud, too fast, too everything. This man felt threatening and overbearing and Winston had an overriding urge to run away.

Realising that this was going on, Winston applied his First Aid for Feelings. Becoming **A**ware that he felt threatened, he brought his focus to his **B**reath and body.

Practising his familiar 5/7 breathing three times, he shuffled his shoulders, and wriggled his toes. Now that he was feeling more present, he used the First Aid for Feelings tools to get curious and realised that this man reminded him of his old boss.

This old boss had bullied Winston relentlessly to the point that Winston left his job. It had taken Winston some time to rebuild his confidence after that experience. Once he'd realised that it was the physical similarity between the two men that had activated his stress state, Winston was able to understand that they were not the same man. This new potential client did not pose a threat and therefore there was no need to be anxious. Winston now had a **C**hoice, he could focus on the similarities between the two men or the differences.

Drawing on his inner coach, he used his self-talk to focus on their differences. His heart stopped racing, his scalp stopped tingling, and all his senses slowed down. By applying his **ABC**, Winston was able to bring himself out of the stress state and into the maintenance state, where he could access his confidence and focus on being the professional he was. The meeting went well and he won the business.

He also made a commitment to himself to care for the agitation once this meeting was over. This is an example of containing and completing feelings. You'll learn about this in the next chapter.

Summary

In this chapter, you have learnt:

- How breathing mindfully helps to release stress and improves your ability to think more clearly

- How breathing mindfully helps you to remain in, or bring yourself back to, the maintenance state, rather than tipping into the stress state

- Why breathing isn't just what you've been doing since you were born and how, with practise, you can use breathing techniques to shift from the stress to the maintenance state

- Why the fact that your breath is always operating in real-time is helpful

- How, by staying in real-time, rather than spiralling into the future or the past, you are able to create the space to find more Choices.

Chapter 06

What will you learn?

How everyone relies on their feelings more than they realise

What your feeling style is, and what a healthy relationship with feelings looks like

Why bothering to read the clues and interpret their meaning is helpful

More details about how you have thoughts and feelings about your thoughts and feelings

How some feelings are historical and why they can be connected with trauma

The difference between trauma with a capital "T" and a lower-case "t"

How feelings are like indicators on a car's dashboard.

Siobhan's story (She/her)

Siobhan was always desperate for her partner to get home from work and take care of the children so she could go for a run. It was her way to deal with feeling trapped — until she began to suffer with debilitating knee pain. Using the techniques described in this chapter, Siobhan realised that her **C**hoice to go running was about "containing" the feeling rather than "completing" it, and wasn't helpful.

By following the clues her feelings were giving her, she was able to make **C**hoices that resolved both her mental and physical discomfort.

You can read Siobhan's full story at the end of this chapter.

06 **Philosophy**

As you learnt in Chapter one, we have feelings for a reason: they provide us with valuable information. To understand this information though, you need to learn their language. We started looking at this in Chapter two. As you begin to get to grips with the language of your feelings — both physical sensations and emotions — you begin to understand the clues they are giving you. They become your guide. Even before you understand what your feelings are trying to tell you, you rely on them subconsciously. Everyone does, more than you realise.

How does everyone rely on their feelings more than they realise?

You probably know someone who says they don't "do" feelings. You might even hold that belief yourself. You may feel confident that you rely heavily on your analytical and rational skills. You may feel that you're pretty level-headed and objective in your decisions and the way you go through your day.

We are here to tell you that this is an illusion. You may believe this, and a lot of people share this belief with you. We all like to think of ourselves as operating from the rational part of our brain for most, if not all, of the time. As you now know, though, that is just a third of our brain. The rest is operating at the level of a dog, or even a crocodile.

Let's give you an example of this. Imagine you're going out on a date with a person who, on paper, is absolutely perfect for you. They share your beliefs and interests, and they have physical characteristics that you find attractive. And you've been introduced by a really good friend, who assures you that you're perfect for each other. You go on a date and they are an absolutely lovely human being, but there is no spark. We're sure you've had an experience like this. We all have in some way, shape, or form. Now, would you go on a second date with that person? The answer is almost certainly no. Why? Because it feels "wrong".

Let's take another example. You go on a date with someone who, on paper, you shouldn't get on with at all. You have nothing — or too much — in common. You meet up, you have a brilliant time. They totally get your sense of humour, they're "sexy as ...", but rationally, analytically, and objectively, a second date shouldn't be on the cards. But would you say no to a second date? Probably not.

Not convinced? Here's a third and final example. You're looking for a new home. You want a set amount of bedrooms, you're settled on the area you want, you're totally clear on your decision making criteria. The estate agent says to you, *"I've got the perfect house for you"*. You walk in, before you've even entered the kitchen, you know this isn't the house for you. By the same token, an estate agent shows you a house that isn't in the location you've specified. It doesn't meet the criteria you've specified either. Yet, when you walk in, there's something about this house that feels like home, and you put in an offer. Or, if you don't, you live to regret it.

These are examples of huge life decisions that aren't based on analytical, objective, rational logic. There are a myriad of other examples just like this: friendships, activities, authors, films. There are lots of activities where rationally, objectively, analytically you "should" be choosing this, but actually, you are choosing that.

Accepting that we all "do" feelings more than we realise is just the start of being able to harness the feelings we have to guide us towards helpful choices. The next step is to understand what your relationship with your feelings is and what your predominant feeling style is.

What is your Feeling style?

BLOCKER ⟵⟶ ENGULFER

Figure 1.3 Feeling style

As you discovered (if you didn't already know it) in Chapter one, not only do we all have feelings, we also all have "feeling styles". There are many different models that describe feeling styles, but at the core of most of them is a spectrum relating to how much, or how little, we engage with our feelings. At one end of this spectrum, are the "engulfers", those of us who are feeling all our feelings all of the time, very intensely. At the other end are the "blockers", those of us who block and rarely "feel" our feelings at all. As you also discovered in Chapter one, there is the cultural component to how we "do" feelings.

In England, for example, the cultural norm, historically at least, has been the "stiff upper lip" attitude towards feelings. Whatever your style is though, whether you're more prone to blocking or to being engulfed by your feelings, it's unlikely to be deliberate or conscious. It will be a learnt behaviour.

Let's start with the blockers. People who block their feelings can be very skilled at using techniques to avoid feeling at all. For example, they might work a lot, focus on other people, help a lot, be very busy all of the time, or use substances. One client, who Thor worked with, literally created a smokescreen between themselves and their feelings, albeit subconsciously. They did this using cigarettes. By following clues, they realised that they were using the action of smoking to help distance themselves from their feelings. When inhaling, they were subconsciously creating a barrier between themselves and the feelings they didn't feel able to experience yet. Aware of this, they chose to keep the coping mechanism for a little longer. However, they made a deal with themself to address it when they had become more confident in their skills and ability to respond to those feelings. In the end, they were able to stop smoking earlier than they anticipated.

Engulfers,[38] on the other hand, have not learnt how to experience their feelings constructively. They feel them in all of their technicolour detail, all of the time. They are often overwhelmed by their feelings and find it difficult to resolve them and move forward.

Very few of us stay at one end of the spectrum all of the time. Most of us tend to travel along the spectrum, depending on, perhaps, the time of day, or where we are in our life stage. Some of us have a different feeling style in our work lives than in our home lives too. When we have a look, though, we are usually able to get a sense that we hang out more towards one end of the spectrum or the other.

Remember that it is more helpful to be curious than critical.

Regardless of where you have a sense of yourself on that spectrum, remember that it is more helpful to be curious than critical. This is especially important if you notice that you are judging yourself, wishing that you were closer to the other end of the spectrum. When you judge yourself, you are less able to have a healthy relationship with your feelings, which is, after all, the driver for self-care and good health.

What does a healthy relationship with your feelings look like?

A person who has a healthy relationship with their feelings: 1) treats their feelings as information; 2) supports themselves to either contain or complete their feelings, as appropriate to the context; 3) trusts what their feelings are telling them and knows how to interpret and support them.

You're learning that **feelings are information** and how important it is to get curious about what that information is trying to tell you. Supporting yourself in terms of choosing whether to "**contain**" or "**complete**" feelings comes next.

Using your **ABC**, you've become **A**ware of the feeling. You've then used your **B**reath and body to keep the top scoop of your brain online. This means that you're now in a position to make a more helpful **C**hoice. The starting point is to choose whether to contain or complete the feeling.

"**Containing**" is when you realise you're feeling something, but you also recognise that the current situation you're in isn't the place for you to get curious. When your **C**hoice is to contain the feeling for a wee bit, or even a lot, longer, the key is to make an agreement with yourself to ensure that you do come back to this feeling and complete it. You can do this by putting a date in your diary. Or, if you don't have a sense of when this is possible, by making an agreement with yourself to care for it as soon as you're able to. If your feeling has been contained and there's been an internal negotiation to contain it, then you do need to make sure you honour that. It's about keeping the promise you've made to yourself.

"**Completing**" then, is when you give yourself time and get curious about the information that your feelings are drawing your attention to. You'll learn a technique for doing this in Chapter eight. For now, once you've got some insight into the purpose of the feeling, you can make a more helpful **C**hoice about what action you want to take.

06 Containing and completing feelings

The way to choose whether to contain or complete a feeling is to check in with yourself about how resourceful you're feeling. This is the **A** of the **ABC**, becoming **A**ware of how you're feeling and whether you feel you've got the resources to get curious about this feeling now. Then do the **B** for **B**reath and body to bring yourself into real-time and increase your access to the part of your brain that can think things through. Now you've got a **C**hoice to make as to whether to contain or complete the feeling. Remember what you're checking here is whether you're feeling resourceful enough to give this feeling the attention and focus it needs.

Here are some questions that can help you make that choice:

1 *Does this feeling feel current? Am I feeling it now in real-time?*

2 *Is it practical to focus on completing this feeling now? Do I have the space and time to do so?*

3 *Does this feeling feel proportionate and appropriate to what's going on?*

4 *Does it feel safe for me to keep following the clues this feeling is giving me on my own?*

5 *Do I need support from a friend or a professional?*

Your answers then guide you to which **C**hoice to make: contain or complete. If it's not practical to focus on completing this feeling now, acknowledge that the feeling is there. Make a commitment to come back to it either at a particular time in the near future, or as soon as is practical.

If any of the answers give you cause to pause, this may be because you've some sort of historical feelings connected to it. These feelings are possibly in relation to a traumatic experience.[39] Let's look at how you can answer those questions in a bit more detail.

What are historical feelings and why are they often connected with trauma?

Look at your answers to the questions above. If the feeling doesn't feel current, proportionate, or appropriate to what's going on, chances are it's an experience associated with something that happened in the past. When you think back to that experience, you still feel the feelings you felt at the time.

If you can still feel the feeling, it's a clear indicator that you've been "containing" and still haven't "completed" this feeling. Without completing it, it's likely that this lingering feeling will continue to affect you.

Now, this is very different from remembering that you had an experience that felt like this. If you remember that you had a feeling that felt like this, but no longer feel the actual feeling, then, you've completed that feeling.

You can have feelings that you haven't completed, about a whole range of things without realising it. They're like bruises. You don't know they're there until somebody touches them, and then — well, ouch, it hurts.

The invitation is to get curious about how some of those feelings are incomplete because you didn't know how to deal with them at the time. Often, they're not "big", they don't paralyse or derail you today, rather, it's almost as if there's a feeling of something incomplete that you just haven't dealt with. If this is the case, this is a past experience that was not traumatic and, by using the technique you'll learn in Chapter eight, you'll be able to complete them.

However, historical feelings can be connected with traumatic events. Such historical feelings not only still feel intense and real, but also affect your behaviours and Choices in ways that are unhelpful to you today.[40]

The difference between trauma with a capital "T" or lower case "t"

We define trauma as: any experience for which we do not have the resources to respond to at the time and complete the feelings associated with that experience.

There are two types of trauma, "big **T**" Trauma and "little **t**" trauma.[41] "Big T" Trauma is where there is a cultural consensus that this is traumatic, e.g. sexual abuse, divorce, a car crash, or a life threatening illness. "Little t" trauma is where the culture you live in doesn't always recognise the experience as being traumatic. These types of trauma are often unseen, such as verbal or emotional abuse, coercive control,[42] or bullying. They're different for each of us and include any type of situation in which we feel vulnerable.

What is traumatic for one person may not be so for another. Nicki, for example, walked away from what could have been a fatal car crash, totally unaffected, with no sense of trauma, yet can feel traumatised if she thinks she's being lied to. So, be kind to yourself about what feels traumatic for you, and respectful of your own experience.

Taking great care with the aspects of your feelings that you experience as traumatic is core to your First Aid for Feelings. Remember the core principle that it is more helpful to be curious than critical. Judging that we shouldn't feel traumatised by an event because it wasn't a "big T Trauma" is not helpful. Neither is judging that we're not feeling traumatised because this is a "big T Trauma".

If it doesn't feel safe to get curious about the feeling, or you feel that you need support from a friend or a professional, take that information seriously. For now, focus on containing the feeling until you can put that support in place. This is where the "**C**" in the **ABC** is so helpful (more on that in Chapter seven). Having a well-stocked First Aid Kit for Feelings is too (more on that in Chapter eleven).

Sounds a bit fluffy? Contain that feeling until you get to the exercises below, where you'll learn how to do this for real. It's not fluffy at all. Trust us.

Trust, of course, is the third aspect of a healthy relationship with your feelings.[43] At the beginning of this chapter, we talked about trusting our feelings regarding whether to go on a second date or choose a house. Knowing when we're having a feeling that is telling us to do something that is unhelpful to us, is healthy. Let's go back to the second date scenario again. You've just had a date with someone who reminds you of a previous partner. You're tempted to go for that second date because you know this dynamic; it feels familiar. Going would be so easy, you could do so on auto-pilot. However, a part of you knows that this feeling is not helpful to you. The last time you had this feeling about somebody, the relationship turned out to be problematic, possibly even toxic. If you have a healthy relationship with your feelings, you will listen to this part, trust it, and not go on that second date. Following the clues that your feelings are giving you, after all, guides you towards making more helpful **C**hoices.

As your relationship with your feelings strengthens, your ability to see more clearly what's going on increases. Your ability to separate out different aspects of what's going on for you strengthens too. You will soon realise that not only do you have thoughts and feelings, you also have thoughts and feelings about your thoughts and feelings.

How do we always have thoughts and feelings about our thoughts and feelings?

As mentioned in the previous chapter, you have thoughts and feelings about your thoughts and feelings. We all do, all of the time. For example, you can feel angry that you're feeling guilty, or you can feel scared that you're feeling happy. We refer to these two layers as the "**core**" thoughts and feelings, and the "**about**" thoughts and feelings. All of us, all of the time, have at least a second layer of feeling wrapped around the core thoughts and feelings.

More often than not it's helpful to start with the **about** thoughts and feelings, before getting curious about the **core** thoughts and feelings.

Figure 6.1 Thoughts and feelings about thoughts and feelings

We've talked about thoughts and feelings as indicators that let you know what's going on for you. With your growing understanding, we want to extend this metaphor to help you get a better sense of how to relate to and understand these indicators. That extended metaphor is to think of your indicators like those on a car's dashboard.

How feelings are like indicators on a car's dashboard

Every car has a dashboard that helps the driver to keep track of how the car is doing. There are four key indicators on every car's dashboard that are often larger and more predominant than the others. These are the speedometer, the rev counter, the fuel gauge, and the water gauge. The speedometer tells you how fast you are travelling. The rev counter tells you how hard your engine is working, and how much effort is going into moving. The fuel and water gauges tell you if you've enough fuel and water to get you to where you need to be. We all have these four key indicators. Then there are the other indicators that can vary from vehicle to vehicle, from person to person. They can include, for example, oil level, brake fluid, and engine temperature gauges.

Figure 6.2 Dashboard

This dashboard concept is helpful in terms of people too. Let's start by looking at the speedometer.

Often when you read psychology books, it's all about slowing down. This is not what we're saying here. The First Aid for Feelings approach isn't about slowing down or speeding up. It's about doing things at an appropriate and helpful speed. Would you drive down a motorway at five miles per hour? Or through a neighbourhood at one hundred miles an hour? No, because that's dangerous. The same principle applies to working to an urgent deadline at five miles an hour, or through historical trauma at one hundred miles an hour.

When you drive through a village in the UK, there is often a sign to slow down. This prompt helps drivers to check their speed. We also have a feeling about our speed in terms of daily living and when we need to slow things down or speed them up.

Now, let's look at the rev counter. In car terms, it's about how hard the engine is working. In human terms it's about effort, how much effort you're putting into an activity. If you're hammering the keyboard, for example, you're applying more effort than needed to get the letters to appear on the screen. If you were going to lift a sofa, you'd need to put in a bit of effort. In general, though, the less effort you put in, the more effortless it's going to be. Turning down the level of tension in your muscles or the tightness in your grip is almost always likely to be helpful, unless you've got a valid reason for keeping it high effort. Checking if you're putting too much or too little effort in is helpful in identifying whether you're in the right gear for the speed that you're travelling at. The first step is to become **A**ware and notice how much effort you're applying.

In terms of fuel and water, well, all humans need enough food and water to have the energy they need to live, to regulate their temperature, and so on. Keeping an eye on these is vital to your self-care and health.

In terms of the additional indicators, it's most helpful to have about five in your dashboard, plus or minus two (so no fewer than three, and no more than seven). Fewer than three is not enough, and is therefore not helpful. More than seven is too many, and also not helpful.

An indicator for you might be that you realise that one of your feeling habits is, *"Why do I always have to do everything? Why is it always on me?"*. You recognise that you always have this feeling or mood under certain conditions. When you start exploring, you might realise that it isn't always "on you". If you're thinking that and feeling that feeling, you've lost access to your top scoop. You've maybe even started crocodiling, which we explained in Chapter four. That *"Why is it always on me?"* thought, then, is one of your indicators.

Another indicator could be in terms of your sleep. If your sweet spot for sleep is for seven hours, and you have a few nights of more or less than that, that's when your sleep indicator comes on. It's likely that there's actually something going on that is affecting your sleep. So, the thing to do is to metaphorically look under the bonnet and ask what's going on that's affecting your sleep.

Another indicator could be in terms of behaviour. It could be that you notice you experience overwhelm when your laundry basket is overflowing, you're overly focussing on other people, or work, for example. Looking after your own basics is getting left by the wayside. This is one of Thor's indicators.

Our invitation to you is to ask yourself what are the indicators that let you know that you're going off track using a green, amber, red code. Remember, though, that wherever you're on each indicator is not a permanent state. None of us are in a fixed state, for example, always in green, for anything, and neither should we be. That would be disproportionate and inappropriate in many circumstances. It would also suggest that you're always staying in a safe space and not opening yourself up to possibilities and untapped potential.

Choosing to go into red for valid reasons like bungy jumping just because you like the adrenaline rush, for example, or learning a new skill, is how we grow, expand, and check out who we really are. The key is to do so consciously with intention.

However, if the brake fluid light on the car's dashboard is blinking red, would you just take the bulb out and keep driving? Or, would you take the car to the garage and do something about it? Once you get a sense of your indicators, there might be things for you that act like, for example, your brake fluid light. There might be things for which, when that brake fluid light starts blinking amber or red, you say, *"Right, let's bring in the professionals"*.

This is how you strengthen your self-relationship so that different parts of you are connected and in tune with how you're actually doing in real-time.

When you start to put some of the feelings that you struggle with in your dashboard, you will train yourself to look out for them. Spotting them when they get to amber, before they get to red, will therefore become easier.

This is a hallmark of a healthy relationship with feelings.

Practice

Exercise 6.1: What's the state of your relationship with your feelings?

Use three to five words that describe your relationship with yourself as it is now:

....

....

....

....

....

....

....

How would you score the state of your relationship now on the scale of zero to ten, with zero being non-existent and ten being the best it can be. Circle the number that feels true for you now.

0 1 2 3 4 5 6 7 8 9 10

Exercise 6.2: Negotiating containing or completing?

6.2.1 Bring to mind a situation when you were struggling with a feeling and were able to stay with that feeling and complete it. Write down your thoughts about what was going on for you, and how you found your way to complete that feeling.

6.2.2 Bring to mind a situation when you were struggling and it wasn't helpful to stay with that feeling and complete it. Here are some questions to help you:

- What was going on for you in this situation?

- Why wasn't it helpful to stay with that feeling and complete it in that moment?

- What kind of agreement could you have made with yourself to contain the feeling at that point, with the intention of coming back to complete it later?

- When could you have come back to complete that feeling? Bear in mind that you may have needed the support of a friend or professional to help you do this.

- How could you talk to yourself to help yourself negotiate containing it for now and coming back to this later? Imagine you're talking to a loved one who's in this situation, what would you say to them?

Exercise 6.3 Your dashboard?

6.3.1 What lets you know when you're in the green, amber, or red state for the four indicators that we all share?

Speed (how fast or slow are you walking / talking / eating?)

Green ....

Amber..

Red..

Rev counter (how much effort are you applying?)

Green ....

Amber ....

Red ....

Food (are you eating enough, too much, or too little?)

Green ....

Amber ....

Red ....

Water (are you drinking enough, too much, too little?)

Green ....

Amber ....

Red ....

6.3.2 Identify between three and five indicators that let you know that you're not OK, and that are specific to you. It can take some time to identify your indicators, so start with just one or two. Here are a few examples to give you an idea: *"My lips are dry"*, *"My laundry basket is overflowing"*, *"I am being clumsier than usual"*.

Indicator one:

Green ....

Amber ....

Red ....

06

Indicator two:

Green ....

Amber ....

Red ....

Indicator three:

Green ....

Amber ....

Red ....

Indicator four:

Green ....

Amber ....

Red ....

Indicator five:

Green ....

Amber ....

Red ....

Exercise 6.4: Reflecting on what you've learnt

Now that you've learnt more about your relationship with yourself, how and when you can contain and complete feelings, and what your personal indicators are, what have you learnt about:

· What it was like to do these exercises? Was it, for example, easy, informative, difficult, or confusing?

· Was it easier or more difficult to learn about your relationship with yourself than you expected?

· How aware were you before doing these exercises about your experience and the answers you've written down?

· Thoughts and ideas you're having about how you could respond differently to what's going on?

What are you learning about yourself?

I am learning that I ....

....

....

....

....

....

....

....

....

06 Siobhan's story (She/her)

Siobhan, a mum to three young children, struggled to get to the end of the day juggling her work and family responsibilities. She took to going for a run the minute her partner came home from work, just to get away from the house and deal with her sense of feeling trapped.

Her overriding feeling was, *"I've got to get out of here"*. To begin with, it was really helpful. However, because she never addressed what was causing it, it soon stopped being helpful. In fact, it became obsessive and led to Siobhan suffering with knee problems.

Encouraged to think about her feeling style, Siobhan recognised that she was more towards the blocker end of that spectrum. She was blocking her feeling of anger by "running away" from it. She recognised that this was stopping her from completing the anger because she hadn't understood what was causing it, and what she needed to do about it. Getting curious about why she struggled to complete feelings like anger, she realised that some of her anger related to her own childhood. Her mother had also struggled with anger, and her father had been absent. Siobhan realised there was a "lower case t trauma" connected to her feeling of anger that she had never completed.

Sharing this revelation with her partner, they committed to sitting down together once the kids were in bed, rather than continuing to facilitate her "running away" behaviour. She realised that it was more helpful to choose *"I want to take care of my feelings"* than *"I've gotta get out of here"*. The conversation also helped Siobhan to realise that it would be helpful to seek support from a professional.

They decided to do this end of day check-in regularly. At first they used this time to talk about Siobhan's experiences of needing to run. Doing this was helpful because it ensured that issues were dealt with. When he saw how helpful this was for Siobhan, her partner started to use this opportunity to talk about his experiences too. They have kept this reflection time in their daily routines to this day and it continues to benefit not just them, but their children too.

Summary

In this chapter, you have learnt:

- How everyone relies on their feelings more than they realise

- What your feeling style is, and what a healthy relationship with feelings looks like

- How following clues about the information your feelings are giving you will help you to address what's going on

- How you have thoughts and feelings about your thoughts and feelings

- How some feelings are historical and can be trauma-based

- How feelings are like indicators on your car's dashboard.

You're now ready to learn why **C**hoice is so important and why you may feel you don't have a **C**hoice, even when you do.

Chapter 07

What will you learn?

Why, if you feel like you don't have a choice, you're "crocodiling"

That, even if you don't have a choice about what happens to you, you can develop the skills to enable you to always have a choice about how you respond

Why your brain is wired to assume everything is a threat until proven otherwise

Why the ability to make choices is a skill rather than a talent

How to prepare yourself to find your way through an experience over which you feel you have no choice or are struggling with.

Asa's story (He/him)

Asa's family liked to raise a glass. So, when he stopped drinking as a way to control symptoms of pain and fatigue, it came as quite a shock to them. His brother teased him relentlessly, calling him a health nut and worse. Asa's pattern was to react, trying to get his brother to understand. This was exhausting.

Using this chapter's methods, Asa recategorised the level of threat his brother posed and chose to change his response. It worked a treat, as you will find out at the end of this chapter.

07 Philosophy

Having learnt about the **A** (**A**wareness) and **B** (**B**reath and body) of First Aid for Feelings' **ABC**, you began to learn about the **C** (**C**hoice) in the previous chapter. Specifically, you learnt about how your feelings provide you with the information you need to help you make a **C**hoice about what would be most helpful to do next.

Sometimes, though, it can feel like you literally don't have a **C**hoice.

Why, if you feel like you don't have a choice, are you "crocodiling"?

If you feel like you don't have a **C**hoice, it is a sure indicator that the part of your brain that can see the bigger picture and think through choices has gone offline. You're **crocodiling**, not **responding** but **reacting.**

Reacting is when you instinctively react to a situation, like pulling your hand back from a hot stove. In that situation, pulling your hand away from the hot stove, completing an action before you've had time to think about it, serves you. By the time you've thought through the issues of leaving your hand on a hot stove, for example, you'll have severely burnt your hand. Sometimes, reaction is essential to save you from harm. Sometimes you need to be able to react quicker than you can think.

Responding is when you access your ability to see the bigger picture, which in turn enables you to see **C**hoices, and then choose the most constructive one.

Remember, in the stress state, resources are diverted away from the brain to systems like the big muscle groups. Therefore, the sense of threat can get in the way of your ability to think, in turn limiting your ability to recognise the **C**hoices you may have. Because you're less able to see **C**hoices in that moment, the feeling that you're choiceless is likely to intensify the feeling of threat. This then drives up your stress hormones, like adrenaline, rather than easing them, which creates a vicious cycle.

The "fight or flight" of the fight-or-flight–or-freeze response

Any experience that feels like *"I don't like it here"*, *"I have no choice but to be here"*, or *"There's nothing I can do"* creates a lot of adrenaline. Faced with such an experience, all of your effort goes into trying to get out. Your survival fight-or-flight-or-freeze mechanism is in full force. You either try to punch (metaphorically or otherwise) your way out of the situation, you run away, or you become paralysed, collapse, or freeze.

This is because when you feel like you've got no **C**hoice, you feel trapped. You feel like there's no way out, like you're cornered. This feeling of being trapped is a deeply uncomfortable experience. Your survival instinct goes into overdrive, and you'll do anything to get free.

In nature, animals will gnaw off their legs to free themselves if they're caught in a trap. If you've seen the movie *127 Hours*, you'll know that humans are also capable of severing limbs in order to escape. Sure, the fight response of severing limbs example may feel a little unrelatable, so let's tell you about Leslie. She was stressed about getting all the Christmas presents bought and in a rush to get into her local shopping mall. Standing outside in the freezing cold, she was struggling to get the door open. Crocodiling, she put more and more effort into opening the door with no success. A kind stranger then tapped her on the shoulder and pointed out that the way to open the door was to push, not pull.

Can you relate to Leslie's experience? What examples can you think of?

The "freeze" of the fight-or-flight-or-freeze response

Let's turn our attention to "freeze". Have you ever gone into freeze and not been able to make the most basic and obvious **C**hoices, like taking off a jumper in order to cool down? Again, this is because the crocodile part takes over and you haven't got access to the part of the brain that remembers the connection between overheating and jumpers. In fact, the crocodile part of the brain might not even realise you're overheating, you might just be feeling increasingly frustrated.

Another example you may be able to relate to is where you were unable to respond to what was going on, only to think afterwards *"I wish I'd said this"* or *"If only I'd done that".*

When you feel like you can't either fight your way out of a situation or run away from it, you go into freeze, you shut down. It's almost as if the lights have gone out and nobody's at home.

Research using functional magnetic resonance imaging (MRI) technology has established that people who've suffered trauma show *"... significantly less activation ..."* in parts of the brain.[44] This research doesn't aim to establish a connection with your ability to make **C**hoices when in this state. However, it's another piece of the puzzle to understand why you struggle to see your **C**hoices at that moment.

What's interesting about this experience is that you can feel this way even though you're not actually trapped. Even though there are options available to you that you just can't see. Therefore, when you feel like you haven't got a **C**hoice, it's a huge clue that you're crocodiling. And, where there's a clue, there's a **C**hoice.

Research into survival psychology[45] backs this up. In fact, it has been shown that people who could have survived a plane crash literally died in their seats because their survival response was to freeze. Going into freeze meant their bodies shut down to conserve energy. This included losing peripheral vision, the result being tunnel vision, both literally and metaphorically, meaning they couldn't see any options. This lost them the valuable seconds or minutes they needed to take action and get out. Meanwhile, those whose survival responses were "fight" or "flight" took action, got out, and survived.

Reminding yourself that just because you perceive you don't have any **C**hoices doesn't mean you don't have any **C**hoices is helpful. It gives you a lever to crack open the perspective that you might, actually, have some choices. It's helpful to recognise that, even if you have no **C**hoice about what is happening to you, you can develop the skills to always have a **C**hoice about how you respond to it.

Viktor Frankl, who we first introduced in Chapter three, famously said, *"Between stimulus and response there is a space. In that space is our power to choose our response. In our response lies our growth and our freedom."*

But how do you find that space that Viktor Frankl is talking about? The key is to understand that your brain is wired to assume the worst.

Why your brain is wired to assume everything is a threat until proven otherwise

Faced with any perceived threat, your brain is wired to assume everything is a tiger first. From a survival standpoint, this makes sense. Let's take a closer look.

Think of a threat in terms of the likelihood of it happening, and then the impact of it happening. With these two factors in mind — likelihood and impact — here are four animals that illustrate this: cats, dogs, wolves, and tigers.

Assuming you like cats, the likelihood of meeting a cat is quite high and if you were to see one you'd likely go and stroke it because the impact of that encounter going badly is a scratch.

Assuming you like dogs, the likelihood of meeting a dog is, again, reasonably high. If you encountered one, you'd pause ever so briefly to check how friendly it looks and then likely go and say hello. The worst impact would be a bite. You might need some stitches and a tetanus jab but rarely is there serious harm.

Assuming you like wolves, the likelihood of meeting a wolf is significantly less than cats and dogs but the impact if that encounter goes badly is significantly worse. Even if you really like wolves, you wouldn't approach one without some consideration in terms of protective gear or expert advice. However, if you're well prepared, the encounter may be well worth doing and, in fact, could be rather magical.

Finally, the likelihood of meeting a tiger is low, but if you did, the impact of that encounter could be life-threatening. Even if you're extremely fond of tigers, before going anywhere near one, you'd take great precaution to minimise the potentially life-threatening impact of it going badly.

By assuming everything is a tiger before proven otherwise, your brain is wired to prioritise your survival and safety. To achieve this mission, the costs to your energy and state is justified. You may not be happy, your health may be suffering, but at least you're alive.

Mission accomplished.

Now imagine if the brain was wired to assume everything was a cat first. By the time you realise that what appears to be a cat is actually a tiger, you could be dead.

Getting curious about whether what you perceive to be tigers are actually tigers is therefore instrumental to opening up the possibility of Choice.

Training your brain to not assume it's a tiger but to make the Choice to check and then downgrade the risk as appropriate, is a skill and takes practise. Recognising that you have a Choice to do that is therefore one of the most powerful insights and gifts you can give yourself.

How there is always a Choice

Often, you may feel like you don't have a Choice. At this point, it can be interesting to do a thought experiment and ask *"Is it helpful?"*, rather than *"Is it true?"*. This is one of the main reasons why we always champion that question. It may feel true that you don't have a Choice, but it will almost certainly not be helpful. It's much more likely to feel helpful to imagine the possibility of Choices. We almost always have more Choices than we think.

Shifting your mindset from *"Is it true that I do not have a Choice?"* to *"Is it helpful to think that I don't have a Choice?"* opens up the possibility that there might be some Choices. You might not have seen them yet, but they might be there.

Now, if you're suspicious of the concept of "thought experiments", it might be helpful to remember that Albert Einstein was a great proponent of this way of opening up possibilities. Indeed, without thought experiments, he may never have arrived at his theory of relativity.

With the possibility of a thought experiment, the next step is to ask yourself, *"Well, if I had a Choice, what might that be?"* When you perform this thought experiment, you're deliberately accessing your creative mind; the top scoop part of your brain. The crocodile part of your brain is no longer in charge. The top scoop, that part of your brain that's capable of analysing and imagining, is now available to you. Knowing how to deliberately access this part of your brain is not a talent, it's a skill, and, as with all skills, it can be learnt.

Why is the ability to make Choices a skill rather than a talent?

Remember neuroplasticity that we talked about in Chapter four, and how the London cab drivers had created more neural pathways than the New York cab drivers? Well, this shows how humans can develop new ways of thinking by training our brains to repeatedly experiment with our thinking.

Just like those cab drivers, when you repeatedly get curious about possibilities, you strengthen the neural pathways to the part of your brain that handles curiosity. As your neural pathways get stronger and stronger, you'll start to be able to find more possibilities in a range of situations.

This approach of deliberately strengthening and cultivating your ability to see Choices in and of itself, is a Choices.

The way you approach a situation over which you feel you have no Choice doesn't have to remain fixed. What we mean here is that, if you habitually respond in a certain way to external limitations, it doesn't have to stay this way. However, unless you realise that the way you are responding is a habit, a feeling style, rather than a truth, it will stay this way. History will keep repeating itself. Once you do realise this though, you can open yourself up to finding alternative ways through experiences, where previously you felt you had no Choice.

How do you do this? How do you find your way through an experience over which you feel you have no choice or are struggling with?

The first thing is to recognise that you feel that you have no Choice, or are struggling, and are therefore crocodiling. This is not a "you" thing, it's a human thing. This is biochemistry in action. This Awareness (the A of our ABC) is the thing that opens up the possibility of feeling differently about what is going on. Before realising this, you won't be able to experiment with creating **C**hoice about how you respond to what is happening to you.

When you recognise that you have a **C**hoice about how you approach your circumstances, something fundamentally changes because you've introduced the possibility of **C**hoice. Introducing the possibility of **C**hoice, though, can feel frightening, disloyal, or like an outrageous claim. We do understand this, so please bear with us. We are not sugarcoating, saying it's all hunky-dory, a wonderful growing experience, or anything of the sort. We know that shit does happen and it can be tough. By changing your response to the difficult situation that you're experiencing, you're in no way condoning it. It's still difficult. Feeling open to **C**hoice in that situation doesn't mean that the situation itself suddenly becomes OK.

There are three typical responses that, from the outset, determine whether you feel you're able to make the **C**hoice at all. They are resignation, acceptance, and surrender.

What are the typical responses to experiencing difficult feelings?

Regardless of dictionary definitions, we all have our own sense of what words mean. Please bear this in mind as you read through our understanding of what these three words mean. It may be different from yours. As ever, we define feelings in terms of the clues they contain. So, with that noted, and an invitation to use your own definitions if they feel more helpful, let's get curious!

Resignation

What is it?

Resignation is a feeling that shows up when something happens that you don't want, or something you want doesn't happen. The key is that you feel you've no influence over it. It feels as if there's no point in taking action, as if you're powerless, or even helpless. Resignation also has a quality of things being "done to you" or "taken from you" against your will or without your permission.

How do you know you are in a state of resignation?

You're likely to hear yourself saying things like, *"That's just the way it is"*, *"There's no use getting so worked up"*, *"I just need to get over it"*, or *"I give up."* You're likely to do behaviours like procrastinate, mutter under your breath, and complain.

Resignation is a passive and disengaged state. This means that when you feel resigned, you don't look for clues and therefore miss out on the valuable information embedded within your feelings. This is because the belief that *"There is nothing I can do"* is inherent in resignation and so there's no point in getting curious.

For sure resignation may feel like the only option at times, particularly in the face of seemingly insurmountable challenges, but, more often than not, it isn't. Becoming **A**ware that this is where you are at is the first step – the **A** part of the **ABC**. Then doing the **B** part of the **ABC**, the **B**reath and body step, to bring your top scoop back online, gives you access to your curiosity.

Once you've taken this step, you then have two other states you may be able to shift your mindset to. Both of these states will enable you to access curiosity and a more helpful **C**hoice. These are the states of "acceptance" and "surrender".

Acceptance

What is it?

Acceptance is the feeling of recognising what's outside your circle of influence, stopping trying to control it, and directing your focus and energy to what's within your circle of influence.[46] It means engaging with the situation in a way that feels helpful to you. More about this later in this chapter.

How do you know you're in a state of acceptance?

You're likely to hear yourself saying things like, *"I don't like what's going on and I don't know how to respond to it yet, and that's OK"*, *"What do I need to learn to move through this experience?"*, or *"I may not like this but I accept that it's happening"*.

When you move towards acceptance, you do not feel powerless, therefore your behaviour is different to that of resignation. You may not have full control but you have some control that gives you agency. You have a circle of influence. You're more likely to be active and engaged, to look after how you're feeling, and, ultimately, to get curious about what's possible.

Surrender

What is it?

Surrender is the feeling of yielding control. Unlike the feeling of resignation, the feeling of control isn't taken from you. Rather, you're choosing to yield control and surrender to the situation. You don't try to change what's happening, there are no feelings of resentfulness, and you move with it.

For some, surrender has connotations of the military dynamic of conquest and submission. For others, there are religious or spiritual connotations. If that is the case for you, get curious about how this word and feeling resonates with you, and check if there is anything there for you to learn? If it doesn't feel helpful for you, don't use it.

How do you know you're in a state of surrender?

Well, you'll hear yourself saying things like, *"I'm going to go with the flow"*, *"I surrender to this experience"*, *"I trust that I'll be OK"*, or *"I trust the process"*. As with the feeling of acceptance, when you surrender you do not feel the powerlessness or resentfulness that comes with resignation. This is because you have made a Choice to surrender. The sense of Choice is the key difference here. However, unlike acceptance, whilst you're engaged with the experience you aren't trying to influence how it feels or what is going on.

Getting curious

Recognising the states of resignation, acceptance, and surrender, you start experimenting with getting curious about the possibility of Choice. So, we've established that whilst you do not always have a Choice about the outside of your experience, you do have a Choice about the inside of it. The key is where you place your focus.

What's within your circle of influence?

When you feel like you can't affect what's going on, you feel powerless. Because this is such an uncomfortable feeling, your inner critic goes into overdrive. We share more about how and why in Chapter nine. Feeling powerless is likely to spill over into other areas of your life. With the fight-or-flight-or-freeze in action, you may find that you start picking fights or faults, retreating and isolating, or even feel paralysed. The most powerful question at this point is, *"What's within my circle of influence?"*.

The circle of influence is about what's within your control to influence. This is about focussing on what you can do within your current capacity – whether that is energy, time, money, or something else. Within this circle you can take action, nurture your sense of having a voice, of being able to take action.

The circle of concern is about being mindful and respectful of what you're concerned about and acknowledging that you don't have influence over what's in this circle. Well, at least not directly. Because you're unable to directly influence what's going on in this circle, focussing on it only serves to amplify your feeling of powerlessness.

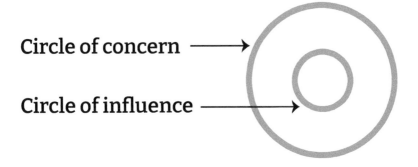

Where is your focus?

Circle of concern ⟶

Circle of influence ⟶

Figure 7.1 Circle of influence / concern

07 What seeds are you watering — what are you focussing on?

Buddhism has the metaphor of watering seeds. The seeds you water grow into strong and sturdy plants. Think of your focus as the water and the object of your focus as your seeds. When you water the seeds of what's in the circle of concern (what's outside of your influence), you grow and strengthen that feeling of powerlessness. The stronger this feeling, the more adrenalised and stressed you are, with potentially detrimental consequences to your health.[47]

When you water the seeds within your circle of influence, you grow and strengthen your feelings of being able to influence, to have a say, to take action. This is about watering the seeds of curiosity, and even courage. This serves you to build the skills of figuring out **C**hoices and finding creative solutions.

In difficult times there is often such a sense of desperation that the focus is all on big actions and big interventions. Whilst this is valid and needed, if this is not within your circle of influence, don't underestimate the power of small actions you are able to take. Every action counts.

Practice

Exercise 7.1: Your crocodile phrase

We all tend to have phrases that we use when we're crocodiling, like *"never mind"* and *"what's the point?"*. What's your phrase? What do you say to yourself when you feel like you've not got a choice?

Your crocodile phrase:...

....

....

....

Now you've identified your keyphrase (it may be more than one), you've got your A, you've got **A**wareness. Do the **B**reath and body step and then check if that phrase is helpful. If it is, great keep using it. If it isn't, think about what might be a more helpful **C**hoice of keyphrase to use instead? Experiment with a few to see which works best for you.

Exercise 7.2: What animal are you seeing

Choose a situation where you felt like you didn't have a **C**hoice. In this situation what was going on, what was the threat? At the time did it feel like a cat, dog, wolf, or tiger? Now, with the benefit of hindsight and what you're learning about how the brain works, get curious, was it really that animal? What can you now see?

What learning can you take from this experience? ....

....

....

....

Exercise 7.3: Your circle of influence

7.3.1 Either using the situation from exercise 7.2 or choosing a new one, let's look at your circle of influence. Write down everything you can think of in that situation that was within your circle of influence. This is about what action you might be able to take and what self-care you could do.

You may find it easier to do this with someone else who can help you think your way through to more curiosity. Remember to use the word "might" to access your curiosity.

7.3.2 Using the same situation, let's look at what's outside your circle of influence. Write down three things or actions that aren't within your capacity or ability.

....

....

....

....

....

Now do a thought experiment. Imagine that you keep focussing on those three things for the next three days. How is that likely to make you feel?

....

....

....

....

Having focussed for three days on what's outside of your circle of influence, would you have been able to do anything from what's within your circle of influence?

Yes   No

Comparing the two, which focus feels more helpful?

....

....

....

....

Exercise 7.4: Reflecting on what you've learnt

Now that you've learnt more about **C**hoice, and what hinders and helps feeling like you've got a **C**hoice, what do you notice about:

- What it was like to do these exercises? Was it, for example, easy, informative, difficult, or confusing?

- Where you habitually place your focus. Do you tend to focus on what's inside or outside your circle of influence?

- How aware were you before doing these exercises about your experience and the answers you've written down?

- Thoughts and ideas you're having about how you could respond differently to what's going on?

What are you learning about yourself?

I am learning that I ....

....

....

....

....

....

....

....

....

07 Asa's story (He/him)

Asa was the middle sibling with an older brother and a younger sister. His family never talked about feelings and were of the mindset that the way to deal with them was to raise a glass. When he started experiencing pain and fatigue in his thirties, one of the first things he was told to do was to reduce his drinking and change his diet. This would help improve his body's digestive process and fuel his recovery. However, when he stopped drinking, his brother started taunting him relentlessly.

Feeling ridiculed and unsupported, Asa would react and try to make his brother understand the seriousness of his symptoms. As Asa didn't want to lose the connection with his family, he felt he had to endure this ridicule. He did so, reacting every time it occurred, hoping that he would somehow change his brother's mind.

When Asa first met Thor, they agreed to start from the assumption that there is a Choice, and got curious about what that Choice might be.

First, Asa realised that, if he thought there was no Choice, he was crocodiling. He also recognised that his reaction was resignation, but, because that feeling was so uncomfortable, his survival response kicked in and he went into fight mode. This would exhaust him.

He also learnt that he was seeing his brother's attitude as a major threat, a tiger. His snowballing fear was that every family member shared his brother's attitude, and he would be rejected. As such, he had resigned himself to fighting every time the taunting began.

Exploring his experience with Thor's support, Asa recognised that his brother wasn't a tiger. Furthermore, no other family member actually participated in these tauntings. He realised that he had a Choice to make. He could continue reacting to his brother's ridiculing, or not. Recognising that he had no control over his brother's beliefs, he chose to say, *"We've had this conversation before, let's talk about something else"* the next time the ridiculing began.

It worked a treat, over time his brother stopped taunting him, and Asa was able to relax in his family's company once more.

Summary

In this chapter you have learnt:

- Why, if you feel like you don't have a Choice, you're "crocodiling"

- That, even if you don't have a Choice about what happens to you, you can develop the skills to enable you to always have a Choice about how you respond

- Why your brain is wired to assume everything is a threat until proven otherwise

- Why the ability to make Choices is a skill rather than a talent

- How to prepare yourself to find your way through an experience over which you feel you have no Choice or are struggling with.

You're now ready to learn about the power of curiosity, which is one of the key skills when finding more helpful Choices.

Chapter 08

What will you learn?

Why curiosity makes it easier to respond to intense feelings and take helpful action

Where your beliefs about curiosity come from

How to use your imagination to drive curiosity

How curiosity goes with the mindset of experimenting rather than solving

A tool for looking deeply and spotting clues to help you make more helpful Choices

How being critical leads to a cognitive cul-de-sac where your thinking gets stuck in a dead end.

Faye's story (She/her)

Faye was struggling with a workplace situation, to a point that she realised it was exhausting her. Familiar with First Aid for Feelings, and using the tools you'll learn about in this chapter, Faye got curious about why she was being so affected by the ongoing situation. Realising that it was due to some deeply embedded beliefs she had about taking responsibility for people in distress, she took action. This action surprised everyone who knew her. She even surprised herself. You can read more about Faye's story at the end of this chapter.

08 Philosophy

You now have an idea about why, when you feel like you don't have a **C**hoice, you are crocodiling. You have also learnt that, while you cannot always control what is happening to you, you can develop the skills to make **C**hoices about how to respond. Having begun to practise the skill of making more helpful **C**hoices, though, you may realise that practising new skills can, at first, be challenging. This is why it's so important to remember that it's always more helpful to be curious than critical.

In this chapter we explain why this reminder phrase is so vital to First Aid for Feelings. We begin by reflecting on why curiosity makes it easier to respond to intense feelings. Curiosity and compassion are the two fundamental principles of First Aid for Feelings. This is why they each get a chapter of their own.

Why curiosity is helpful

Experiencing intense feelings can be difficult. Your feeling style will affect how you respond (remember the two ends of the spectrum — engulfers and blockers). Your culture, values, beliefs, and the fact that you always have thoughts and feelings about your thoughts and feelings will also affect how you respond. Navigating such complexity requires curiosity.[48]

Where do your beliefs around curiosity come from?

Every person on the planet has their own relationship with curiosity. We often think that this relationship is deeply personal, however, we're all steeped in cultural frameworks about what is and what isn't acceptable to think. If you were brought up in the UK, for example, you may well believe that curiosity is a risky thing not to be tampered with — it "killed the cat" after all. Not only that but getting curious "rocks the boat" for goodness sake, and, if you "raise your head above the parapet", well, then, you're sure to invite calamity. It's best then to just "keep calm and carry on" is it not?

Whatever your culture, it's likely that there will be some beliefs about curiosity. Are you aware of what they are? Have a think about what they might be.

It's not only your national culture that shapes your beliefs around curiosity. Other aspects like your faith group, your family, your friends, your socio-economic status, and the time that you're living in also play a part.

Cultural beliefs change over time. Indeed, up until the middle ages, really clever people believed that the Earth was flat and that, if you walked too far, you'd fall off the edge. Today, most of us can't imagine having that belief. We also can't imagine what beliefs we currently have that will be updated by future generations. When we do get curious, though, it can open up many areas of our lives. Surely, it's beneficial to get curious about what **C**hoices we have in any situation, rather than assuming we have none.

So how do you do this? How do you get, and stay curious in the face of adversity? Well, you need to keep all three scoops of your brain online[49] and plug into your imagination.

How does curiosity go with the mindset of experimenting, rather than solving?

According to Jung, Flores, and Hunter, the imagination is a "... complex cognitive construct" involving lots of different parts of your brain.[50] In order to access your imagination then, you first need to do the **A** and **B** of your **ABC**. This ensures you have access to the different parts of your brain that you need to be sure you have enough brainpower to move onto **C**, which is **C**hoice.

What is?

What might be?

Next, you need to shift the focus of your questions, from *"What is?"* to *"What might be?"*. Thinking in hypothetical terms is helpful because, as soon as something becomes hypothetical, you don't need the level of evidence that you request of yourself for things that are definite.

"What can I do about this?" requires you to come up with the actual answers that you can act upon. Contrast that with, *"What might I be able to do about this?"* which engages your imagination so that you can start to do thought experiments. Playing around with possibilities, rather than coming up with actual actionable answers, gives you the freedom to follow the clues that your feelings are giving you.

How does this work then? Well, when you begin to imagine what you might be able to do, you engage the states that are relevant to what you're imagining. If you are imagining something scary, your fight-or-flight-or-freeze response ramps up. Your body goes into the relevant "action mode" fuelled by the adrenaline and related stress hormones.

Shifting your focus from what feels threatening (once you've established it's not a tiger) to imagining what might be possible, changes your state. You move from the stress state of fight-or-flight-or-freeze to the maintenance state. When you imagine something reassuring, empowering, or caring, the feel-good neurotransmitters sometimes referred to as the happy hormones[51] are released. You feel better.

If this sounds far-fetched, think about the last time you were drawn into the world of your imagination whilst watching a film. When running First Aid for Feelings workshops, Thor often recounts going to see "Interview With A Vampire" at the cinema. Thor was in Iceland at the time, nowhere near 20th century San Francisco or 18th century Louisiana, both key locations and time points in the movie. As far as they know vampires do not exist, and yet, Thor felt all the feelings of fear and terror from the comfort of the cinema seat. How can this happen?

Well, it happens because film directors are particularly skilled at knowing how to create certain states. This is why we have genres such as horror and romantic comedy, which follow formulas in order to generate pre-determined states of feeling in us. Knowing this, then, it's possible to turn it to our advantage and play around with movie-making in your imagination. Experiment with questions like, *"What sort of movie am I playing in my mind?"* and *"How is it making me feel?"*. If, for example, the current movie you are playing is *"I don't have a choice"* it's likely to be making you feel disempowered. Instead, start to imagine that there might be some different choices. Begin to experiment with a different movie in your mind and ask how that might make you feel. This will help you to explore potential choices about which course of action to take.

There's more to your imagination than you think

Still sounding too far-out? Think about the neuroscience of imagination. When you haven't done something before you have no reference for it, you haven't laid down the neural pathways. As such, your brain doesn't have a reference for this potential new **C**hoice. The only way to build and strengthen skills, behaviours, and thoughts that will allow you to experience new experiences, is to use your imagination and simulate possibilities.

Surgeons, pilots, and astronauts do this. An integral part of their training is simulation. Athletes in training do too, visualising races without putting in the actual oomph because training to competition level every single day would exhaust them, and possibly lead to injury. They can experiment with potential possibilities without the potential injuries. Then, by simply going through the movements without applying force, they can train their muscle memory. You can do so with your feelings too.

Why is it important to have a tool for looking deeply and spotting clues to help you make more helpful **C**hoices?

Often, when you start to look at your feelings, it can be so overwhelming and confusing that you just don't know where to start. Having a tool for working with your feelings can therefore be helpful.

The tool First Aid for Feelings uses is map-making. This is a bit like when you see a detective on TV solving a case. They have a board and they start with something in the middle. Then they have all these things that come out of that middle like a spider's web. They're making a map of everything that's going on in the case, so that they can visualise all the clues and see where clues might possibly link. There'll always be something you can't see, until you look more deeply.

Solving clues inside your head is hard. The best way to start is to get all of your clues outside of your head. You need a map of the situation or feeling that you're investigating, just like those TV detectives.

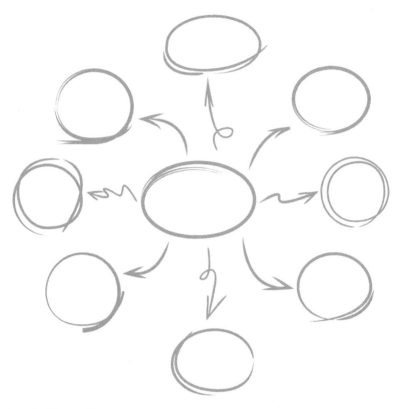

Figure 8.1 Map-making

Start with a piece of paper and, in the middle, write the name of the feeling or experience that you're having, for example, disappointment. Then think about any prompts, memories, or references that connect with this feeling, no matter how obscure or obvious they feel. What you're doing here is downloading your clues onto the paper. Some might lead nowhere, but you will not know this until you check them out. Some may take you straight to the heart of the matter. Then there are some that will take you somewhere else first because you need to solve that before you can address this.

This is what we call "sherlocking". It's a term inspired by the great detective Sherlock Holmes. It refers to "the purposeful process of following the clues your feelings are giving you in order to help you understand the information they contain and make a helpful choice".

Sherlocking

Gerund

Sherlocking is the purposeful process of following the clues your feelings are giving you in order to help you understand the information they contain and make a helpful choice.

Figure 8.2 Sherlocking

Here are our seven sherlocking clue-busting questions to help you with your map-making.

Sherlocking's seven clue-busting questions:

1 *Is it helpful?*

2 *Why bother (investigating)?*

3 *What am I making it mean?*

4 *What's within my circle of influence?*

5 *What information would I be missing out on if I didn't have this feeling?*

6 *Is what I'm thinking, feeling, and doing familiar?*

7 *Is it proportionate and appropriate, or is it historical (linked to something that happened to me in the past)?*

We give you detailed instructions for doing your map-making in the exercise section below.

Sherlocking and map-making guide you to more helpful **C**hoices. You're able to see what's going on in a different way. You're able to make connections and even spot patterns. Remember these are skills you're learning and like all skills, they need practising. For example, spotting patterns can take a while when you're starting out. It's a bit like the children's book we mentioned earlier, "Where's Wally", where Wally, in his striped red and white jumper and hat, is hidden in a crowd of people. In the beginning it'll take you a while to locate Wally but by the time you get to the end of the book you've developed your pattern-spotting skills. You've learnt to look for the red and white stripes and, each time you do that, your neural pathways get stronger and you spot them quicker.

Sherlocking and map-making are used at the **C**hoice step of your **ABC**. However, because it's a top scoop intensive activity, you may need to spend some extra time on the **B**ody and breath stage of your **ABC** to help you. We've got some tips for you on that later on in this chapter.

As you start to map your clues, that is your answers and insights, you'll start to see what you can learn from this experience and take forward with you. This could be about updating beliefs (e.g. that you can't say "no" or that self-care is selfish) and behaviours (like giving yourself enough time to hang up the laundry and not rush). It may be about developing skills, like assertiveness, or learning a practical skill that you'd like to be able to do. This is where you find out what you can think, feel, and do differently.

Now that you have this information you can use it to create a more helpful **C**hoice.

It can take a wee while to get the hang of map-making. It takes practice. Remember Faye from the start of the chapter? Have a look through Faye's map and see how she's done it.

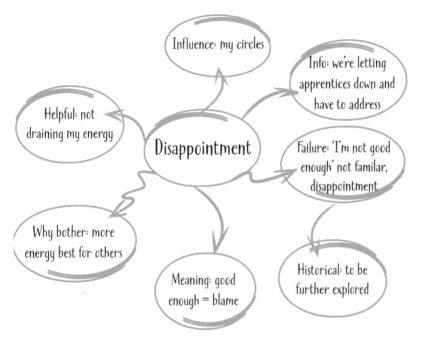

Figure 8.3 Map-making example

Map-making takes brain-power

This level of sherlocking is not about containing, it's about completing. Or at least, completing enough for now. It takes focus and brain-power. Therefore it's something that you do when you're out of the immediate situation and have had the opportunity to reduce your stress state and increase your maintenance state. Remember, this is key to increasing your access to all of your brain. You don't need to be fully calm or relaxed. You just need to be that bit calmer, that bit more relaxed. Here are a few tips to help.

Gear-changing tips to feel a bit calmer

There are ways to help yourself become that bit calmer. You may not be surprised to know that some of these include using your **B**reath and body in order to access your brain.

08 Use your Breath

Sometimes doing the 5/7 breathing three times (3-5-7), or even the 4x4x4 breathing we mentioned earlier, isn't enough to help you feel ready to sherlock to this level. In those situations it can be helpful to do these in sets. This means cranking it up a notch. Experiment with taking the 5/7 to say 7/9 so that you breathe in to the count of seven and out to the count of nine. Do this five times (so it's 5-7-9).

Or take the 4x4x4 and make the breaths and gaps longer by an extra count, so it's 5x5x4. Remember, there are four stages, or sides: the in-breath; the gap between the in-breath and the out-breath; the out-breath; the gap between the out-breath and the in-breath. The count is for how long you hold for each stage or side.

Play around with these numbers. As always with the **B**reath part of the **ABC**, the key is to shift your focus to your breath and deliberately affect your biochemistry. Remember to be respectful of your body and what it's telling you. If you start to feel uncomfortable or dizzy, stop — give your breath and lungs the space to do what feels most helpful.

Use your body

The second part of the B in the **ABC** is the body. In addition to what you've already learnt, like shuffling your shoulders and wiggling your toes, experiment with your sense of touch. Touch has been shown to help stimulate oxytocin (one of the happy hormones) and is "... *associated with some anti-stress effects, lower anxiety, and pain reduction.'*[52] Notice how it feels to place the palm of your hand on the top of your chest. If you're able to, experiment with stroking down from your shoulders to your fingertips, and from your hips down to your toes. The key here is that the direction of the stroking is downwards. Imagine you're stroking a cat or a dog whose hackles are up, you want to go from head to tail, not the other way around. Using that reference, imagine that your nerve endings, just underneath the surface of your skin, are 'up', as if your hackles were up. You want to stroke down from head to toe. Thor refers to this as Central Nervous System stroking, or CNS stroking for short.[53]

Once you're feeling more connected with your **B**reath and your body, you can add some brain teasers to help you limber up for the sherlocking and map-making. Here are a couple that we use, which you may enjoy experimenting with.

Limber up your brain with the "minus seven game"

This is where you give your brain a bit of a work-out. You start with the number 100 and then deduct the number seven, which gives you 93. You then deduct another seven, which gives you 86. Deduct another seven, which gives you 79 — and so on. You'll end up with the number two. Whilst focussing on this, it's impossible to do anxiety thought patterns like snowballing or mental tennis at the same time. Do note that it's highly likely that you'll lose your way. That's fine, just start again, you'll get there.

Warm-up your brain with the "alphabet game"

This is where you use the alphabet, starting with A, then B, then C, and so forth and apply it to a category. You can use categories like names of countries or cities, animals, food, furniture, anything really. Here's what it would look like with the category of countries: Argentina, Brazil, Cuba, Dominican Republic, etc.

The reason these exercises work in getting you ready to sherlock is that they require you to use your brain to work out the next step. Giving your brain warm-up exercises like these shifts your focus away from what was driving up your stress response. This means that you calm down enough to think through what you could do differently.

If you don't get on with those two, experiment with your own brain teasers. There are so many available, there's sure to be some that work for you.

Intuition and gut feel

We focus a lot on how your brain is affected by whether you're more in the stress state or maintenance state. You're learning how to deliberately shift towards being more in the maintenance state to help you maximise your brain-power and therefore your ability to make helpful Choices. But there's more to this than that. When you're feeling calmer and more Aware of your own experience, you're more likely to be able to access other senses. Whether it feels like gut instinct, inner knowing, or something else, it's likely you've experienced intuitive moments giving you helpful insights. Such insights may not have made sense at the time, but later proved to be spot on. Our invitation to you is to get curious about these experiences too and include those clues in your sherlocking.

So, to summarise: it's important to have a technique and a tool to look deeply to spot the clues your feelings are giving you. It helps you get started when you're feeling overwhelmed or confused by getting the information out of your head so your eyes can see it.

It also helps you to keep going when *"Yeah but"* thinking takes you down a cognitive cul-de-sac where you get stuck in a dead end.

> **"Even though I don't know what this means yet, I'm paying attention and am open to spotting more clues. I am here with myself and for myself."**

When you start sherlocking and map-making you're likely to stumble over thoughts like *"yeah but"*. These thoughts may feel like obstacles that are getting in the way. You may feel that you need to ignore them and focus on the positive. This isn't the case. Feelings are information and that applies to all feelings, even the ones that you may consider negative. A *"yeah but"* is a rich source of information. Our invitation to you is to follow the *"yeah but"*, apply the clue-busting questions, and see where the sherlocking takes you.

It's likely that you can't always decipher the clues and tease out the information. This happens. You may not have enough information yet, or you may need more examples to be able to spot a pattern. When this happens it can be helpful to name it for what it is. In these situations, experiment with using this type of phrasing:

"Even though I don't know what this means yet, I'm paying attention and am open to spotting more clues. I am here with myself and for myself."

This phrasing is taken from a technique called Emotional Freedom Technique (EFT), often referred to as tapping. The phrasing has three main components: the opening words "even though", then the "issue" which, in this case, is that you don't know what it means yet, and concludes with an intention. In EFT this last segment is about expressing self-acceptance. This could be *"I truly and completely love and accept myself"* or *"I'm here with myself and for myself"* or *"I'm OK enough"*. Experiment with whatever wording feels helpful to you. It's a great way to stop yourself from thinking yourself into a cognitive cul-de-sac.

How being critical means your thinking gets stuck

When you're being critical, it's a good clue that you're losing access to the part of your brain that can explore choices. In fact, being critical is one of the defining characteristics of losing that access; it demonstrates that you're going into an *"us against them"* mindset. This is a clue that you've not got access to your top scoop and are stuck in the group scoop.

Think about it, when you are being critical, you are usually being critical of someone or something. Before you know it you start blaming. As soon the blame game kicks off, it's too late, you've lost your access to curiosity.

So what happens?

Well, without the curiosity required to create **C**hoices, you drive yourself further and further into the cognitive cul-de-sac, or dead-end, where your adrenaline will keep on rising. Eventually this will take out your group scoop leaving you crocodiling in an *"it's me versus the rest of the world"* mindset.

This is why it's so important to be curious rather than critical.

08 Practice

A message from Thor and Nicki: These exercises are about looking a bit deeper and so we recommend that you've read the previous chapters before doing them. Doing so will mean that you've already got enough understanding and tools to be able to have a helpful experience.

Exercise 8.1: Getting curious about curiousity

8.1.1 It's time to get curious. Explore and complete these three sentences about your beliefs and behaviours about curiosity:

> *I believe that curiosity is* .... (fill in what's true for you)

> *My behaviour in terms of curiosity is* .... (fill in what's true for you)

> *I tend to be curious / not curious* (choose which one is more true to you)

Write down your completed sentences from above and add any other sentences and beliefs that come to mind.

8.1.2 Looking at the completed sentences you have written down. How does it feel to see them? Do they feel helpful? If your answer is "*yes*", that's great — keep them. If they don't feel helpful, get curious about what might be more helpful beliefs and behaviours to have about curiosity.

Exercise 8.2: Limbering up

These exercises are all about limbering up your breath, your body, and your brain to help you get ready to sherlock what's going on. We recommend giving yourself 10 to 15 minutes the first time you do them. Don't be deceived by the simplicity of these exercises. And don't just read and move on, or try them half-heartedly. The learning is in the doing — or as Yoda would say, *"Do or do not, there is no try"*.

8.2.1 Your breath is your gateway to **C**hoice. The purpose of this exercise is to help you strengthen your access to this gateway. The more skilled you become at working with your breath, the easier it'll become to do, meaning you'll become more agile in shifting to a more helpful **C**hoice.

Use the step up version of the 3-5-7 breathing technique and take it to 5-7-9 or the 4x4x4, whichever is more helpful to you. Now deliberately play around with the numbers. When you're doing any version of the 3-5-7, remember the key focus is on the out-breath being longer. If you're doing the 4x4x4, remember that the focus is on giving your lungs that structural workout, so increase the number on all four sides evenly. You'll find more about these exercises in Chapter five.

8.2.2 The purpose of this exercise is to remind your brain that there is more to you. Start connecting with your body by doing something physical. Remember you want to amplify the **B**reath and **B**ody **(B)** aspect of the **ABC** technique that you learnt in Chapter three. In addition to shuffling your shoulders and wiggling your toes, experiment with movements such as walking up and down stairs, doing a few dance moves, or stretching.

Get curious about what the sensations you're experiencing feel like, and where in your body you're feeling them? Describe these to yourself out loud. For example, *"I'm feeling a tightness in my chest and my knees feel a bit cold."* Notice what it feels like when you hear yourself describe your sensations in detail.

Then experiment with the CNS stroking and soothing the hackles, or the nerve endings, of your central nervous system, that we described earlier. Remember that with animals it's head to tail and with humans it's head to toe, always moving downwards. Do this a few times and then check in again with your sensations and notice if there's been a change.

8.2.3 The purpose of this exercise is to interrupt the thoughts and feelings that you're currently experiencing and to prepare your brain to do some sherlocking.

Have some fun with the minus seven game and the alphabet game detailed above. Or, if neither of those feel helpful, experiment with giving your brain a workout using something that works for you. Think of athletes limbering up before training or a performance. This is what you're doing.

Exercise 8.3: Start sherlocking

8.3.1 You're now ready to do some sherlocking. You may prefer to do this on your own, or feel it would be helpful to do this with someone you trust. Go with what feels most helpful to you.

It's rarely obvious how long sherlocking a situation will take. Start with half an hour and see how that feels. You don't have to do it all in one go, so no pressure there. You can always keep your notes and come back to your sherlocking and map-making at another time.

Get yourself some different coloured pens and as big a piece of paper as you can find to do your map-making. Notebooks and flipchart-sized sheets are great, but not necessary.

Choose a situation where you weren't able to care for and complete the feeling you were experiencing. It can be helpful to start with something that doesn't feel intense. This means you're not sherlocking intense feelings whilst you're learning how to do this. You can save these for when you're feeling like you're getting the hang of it.

Give the situation or feeling a name or a title. This is the word you'll write in the middle of your map. The name can be descriptive and describe what happened, or it can be the name of the person or location where this happened. You can also use a word that acts as a reference, such as a colour like "red", or a type of weather like "stormy". You can even give it a code name. Whatever feels most helpful to you.

Start applying the seven clue-busting questions. It can be helpful to start with them in order, but if you find that it's helpful to do them in a different way, go with that.

Go gently with yourself. Take breaks as you need to. Play music that you like whilst you're doing your map-making, if you find that helpful. Brew your favourite cuppa, if that helps. This is about making this experience supportive and helpful. If you've done this exercise solo, it can be helpful to connect with someone you trust afterwards, even if you don't talk about what you've discovered. The purpose of that is to strengthen a feeling of connection and belonging. This releases the happy hormones and helps you feel better.

This exercise is about finding the clues that help you to complete the feeling you're experiencing.

In the next exercise you'll start exploring more helpful Choices.

8.3.2 Imagine you're at a junction. Before you are two paths. You have the choice of continuing down the path of your habitual Choice,[54] or you can start to experiment with the path of your new more helpful Choice.

Imagine that you continue down the path of your habitual Choice for the next few days, the next few weeks, months, and years. As you imagine that future prospect of your habitual Choice becoming stronger and stronger, how does that make you feel? Would this path be helpful?

Imagine you experiment with the path of your new Choice. How could that feel over the next few days as you practise and strengthen the neural pathways? Next, imagine you're a few months into the future and you've developed those skills, and that this is now how you feel more and more of the time. How does that feel? Then fast forward for the next few years, and then some more years where the new Choice is so habitual to you that you can't really remember what it felt like to do your old Choice. How does that feel?

Which path do you choose?

Exercise 8.4: Reflecting on what you've learnt

Now that you've experimented with sherlocking and map-making, what do you notice about:

· What it was like to do these exercises? Was it, for example, easy, informative, difficult, or confusing?

· Your beliefs and behaviours about curiosity? Are you spotting anything new or making connections that may not have been visible before?

· How aware were you before doing these exercises about your experience and the answers you've written down?

· Thoughts and ideas you're having about how you could respond differently to what's going on?

08 What are you learning about yourself?

I am learning that I ....

....

....

....

....

....

....

....

....

....

....

....

....

Faye's story (She/her)

Faye, a senior executive in an organisation, agreed to take on responsibility for mentoring colleagues who were about to embark on two years of study for their professional qualifications. Little did anyone know that COVID-19 would mean they would be studying from home.

As time went on, it became clear in the monthly catch-up calls that her students were struggling to apply their learning to their jobs. At least half an hour of each call was spent teaching them the **ABC** of First Aid for Feelings to help them cope with the feelings of anxiety they were experiencing. This meant half an hour less focussing on actual coursework.

By month five, Faye, who did not identify as a quitter, was dreading the calls and wanting to quit the role. Curious about why these sessions were taking so much out of her, she turned to her own First Aid for Feelings to sherlock the clues, completing a mind-map.

Completing the mind-map, Faye became **A**ware of a heavy sense of responsibility for the students' well-being. She felt she would be failing them if she didn't make the organisation aware that what had worked before lockdown wasn't working now. This helped Faye identify three possible courses of action: she could carry on for another year and a half and do her best; she could talk to her organisation about her concerns and identify ways to do things differently; or she could resign.

Option one was not an option. She just didn't have the energy to sustain this, especially as it flew in the face of her personal values. Forcing the students through the course without any adaptations felt unfair, cruel, and cowardly. Option three, quitting, felt unfair, cruel, and cowardly too.

So, Faye consulted with her employer and advised them to devise an online learning approach that would make the students feel more supported. And she stepped back from the role, having found someone suitable to replace her.

Moreover, she also realised that feeling responsible was a life theme that often led to "I'm not good enough" experiences. She committed to working on this with the help of a professional.

	Question	Faye's answer
1	Is it helpful?	No. It's draining me of energy and negatively impacting all of my work, and my peace of mind.
2	Why bother investigating?	So I can get my energy back and get back to making the positive difference I pride myself on.
3	What am I making it mean?	I think I am making the fact my students are struggling mean that I am not good enough. I am blaming myself for their distress.
4	What is within my circle of influence?	Whether I continue with this role. Whether I do or don't, how I communicate what I am thinking, feeling, and doing with our leadership team – and my students.
5	What information would I be missing out on if I didn't have this experience?	That we're letting our people down and we need to do something about it.
6	Is what I'm thinking, feeling, and doing familiar?	God yes! I've always felt responsible for any sentient being who appears to be experiencing suffering.
7	Is it proportionate and appropriate, or is it historical (linked to something in the past)?	It's historical because it feels disproportionate.

Figure 8.4 Map-making example table

Summary

Throughout this book, we've been championing curiosity. In this chapter, you've learnt why we've dedicated a whole chapter on this core First Aid for Feelings principle.

Specifically, you've learnt:

- Why curiosity makes it easier to respond to intense feelings and take helpful action

- Where your beliefs about curiosity come from

- How to use your imagination to drive curiosity

- How curiosity goes with the mindset of experimenting rather than solving

- A tool for looking deeply and spotting clues to help you make more helpful **C**hoices

- How being critical leads to a cognitive cul-de-sac where your thinking gets stuck in a dead end.

You may have found the penultimate exercise more difficult than previous exercises, which is why we recommend you begin with something that did not feel too intense. Or, you may have found it easy, and feel ready to tackle a more complex situation.

Whatever your experience, the key is to be compassionate with yourself. First Aid for Feelings is a skill and like all skills it takes practice and self-compassion.

Talking of self-compassion, which is the other fundamental principle of First Aid for Feelings, you're now ready to learn why it is so vital.

Chapter 09

What will you learn?

How your relationship with yourself is your longest and most challenging relationship, making it the most important relationship you'll ever have

How this relationship is made up of various parts, including your inner critic, your inner coach, and your inner child

How your culture influences your relationship with yourself and that, as well as a personality, you have a "culturality"

How it's important to keep it real and why positive isn't always helpful

Why taking your struggles and fears by the hand is the more powerful option

Why neglecting your relationship with yourself can be as, or more, detrimental as neglecting any other relationship

Why putting your oxygen mask on yourself first is not a cliché.

Yadid's story (He/him)

Five-year-old Lucy refused to go to bed at her grandparents' house. She was convinced that monsters lived beneath it. Her Uncle Yadid supported her to get curious and sherlock whether her fears were based on reality, or on a movie she'd recently watched. There's a lot to be learnt from taking your fears and your inner child by the hand in this way, as this chapter explains.

09 Philosophy

Now you understand why curiosity is so much more helpful than criticism when it comes to responding to feelings, it's time to turn your curiosity towards the topic of "self-compassion".

Take a look at your social media streams, or the well-being pages of any magazine or newspaper: "self-compassion", "self-love", "self-care", whatever the label, it's ever-present. Phrases such as *"Remember to put your oxygen mask on yourself before assisting others"* may seem trite, but they exist for a reason. After all, if you cannot sustain being well, or alive, how can you help others?

In this chapter we're going to explore self-compassion in-depth. First though, let's clarify what self-compassion actually means.

Kristin Neff is a leading author on the subject of self-compassion. She talks about self-compassion as having three main components: **self-kindness**, **common humanity**, and **mindfulness**.

Self-kindness is being kind and understanding toward oneself in instances of pain or failure, rather than being harshly self-critical.

Common humanity is perceiving one's experiences as part of the larger human experience, rather than seeing them as separating and isolating.

Mindfulness is about holding painful thoughts and feelings in balanced awareness, rather than over-identifying with them.[55]

This means that your relationship with yourself is at the heart of self-compassion.

But, why bother developing self-compassion? The short answer is because your relationship with yourself is, without a doubt, your most important relationship, so you'd better make it a good one.

Your relationship with yourself is the most important relationship you have

Your relationship with yourself is the longest relationship you'll ever have. From your first breath to your last, no-one else is with you every breath of the way.

Given that, in the words of mindfulness expert, Professor Jon Kabat-Zinn,[56] *"Wherever you go there you are"*, it's vital that you can both live with yourself and care for yourself. Self-care, therefore, is not just a *"nice to have"*. It's essential.

However, self-care is one of the most difficult skills to learn. People often place themselves, and the people they support, at considerable and significant risk of illness or injury, through lack of self-care. Why? Because of the misguided belief that self-care is selfish.

When you constantly put off looking after your own needs because you believe that someone else's needs should take priority, you're missing the point. When you run out of energy, health, resources, and suchlike, you're not going to be able to help that person at all, or anyone else for that matter.

So, how do you start to take better care of yourself? It's helpful to understand a little more about what exactly is going on inside your head. Your relationship with yourself comprises many parts, including your inner critic and inner coach.

You also have an inner child, that part of you that feels younger and more childlike.

Knowing a little more about each will help you to strengthen and guide your relationship with yourself.

Conscious thoughts and unconscious thoughts

You may not be aware of it, but you're continuously talking to yourself in terms of the thoughts you're thinking. And this thinking can be separated into two groups: conscious thoughts and unconscious thoughts.[57]

Conscious thoughts are the thoughts that you're **A**ware of, the thoughts you can "hear" if you just listen. *"I'm hungry"*, for example, or *"I'm happy"*. Unconscious thoughts are the thoughts that you do so habitually that you're not conscious of them at all. *"I'll never be good enough"*, for example.

Sounds intense, doesn't it? You're right, it really can be intense. But there are things you can do to ease the intensity.

Historically, it was thought that the unconscious mind does up to two million thoughts a second, and the conscious mind does between five and seven thoughts a second. Over the last few decades, those kinds of numbers have been called into question. Regardless of the actual numbers, however, it's fair to say that a lot more happens in your unconscious mind than in your conscious mind. It's therefore well worthwhile getting curious about what goes on in your head.

Understanding your self-talk

What goes on in your head, those conversations you have with yourself, is called self-talk. Understanding it is important because the quality of your self-talk directly affects the quality of your self-relationship.

Your self-talk is essentially like a conversation, although often it can feel like an argument. It's something everyone does and the different "voices" in the conversations are referred to as "parts" in most schools of psychology.[58]

Different parts often show up in the way you speak. You may have heard yourself say, *"A part of me wants this and another part of me wants that."* Sound familiar? The most vocal part in your self-talk is often the inner critic.

How to recognise your inner critic

This is the part of you that is critical. It says things such as *"you idiot"*, *"silly me"*, or even *"I shouldn't have done that"*. Whether it's blatantly critical or more subtle, the message is a criticism of you.

The inner critic often speaks in "shoulds" and "musts", so listen out for these words. It may not seem obvious but this part does have a purpose. It can be helpful. Indeed, its role is to be your personal risk manager, reminding you of the norms and values of your social group. This helps ensure that you're accepted and not rejected.

When you're young, your parents or caregivers are responsible for this social training. They teach you to say *"please"* and *"thank you"*, to share your toys, to not hit others, how to cross the road safely, and so on. As you grow up, this function becomes internalised, and you develop an inner critic, which serves to keep you safe from harm. This applies not only to physical harm but also mental and social harm.

More about that soon. First, a true story to illustrate why the brain is wired to care about other people's opinions.

Yamato's story[59]

Let's time travel to Japan, 2016, and the story of Yamato, a seven-year-old boy. He'd been asked repeatedly by his dad to stop throwing stones at a neighbour's car. Dad eventually became exasperated and decided to teach his son a lesson. He drove Yamato to the woods and left him there to think about his actions. When he returned 20 minutes later, Yamato had wandered off into the woods, where there were bears and other wild animals. Unable to find his son, dad called the authorities, who later summoned the national army to help with the search. It made the headlines nationally and internationally, and catalysed a countrywide discussion about parenting methods.

It took six days to find Yamato. How did he survive? He'd been able to find shelter in some army barracks. He was tall enough to reach the handle and let himself in and old enough to realise he needed to close the door behind him to keep himself safe from wild animals. He was also able to find water and biscuits and keep himself safe until found.

Had he been a bit shorter, had he not realised to close the door behind him, or had he not found biscuits and water, Yamato's life would have been at risk. He was truly in a life-threatening situation.

09

Remember the animal risk model in Chapter seven? Well, this was a life-threatening situation, a tiger. When children are rejected by caregivers, the risk to life is real. Humans are wired to avoid being rejected, so, we develop our inner critics as a means to manage that risk.

Fast forward to adulthood, and some of that programming will be out of date. The consequences of rejection may not be as severe now that you're an adult. Even if someone was, for example, to stop giving you food, chances are you can get it yourself. Thinking back to chapter seven, the risks have gone from tiger to cat, making it a very different reality.

Humans have the longest childhood of all mammals and are dependent on caregivers for longer than any other mammal. This makes the inner critic even more important as it helps you function in your social and cultural environment.

Contrary to what you may have read elsewhere, we don't advocate trying to ignore or get rid of your inner critic. Knowing the purpose of your inner critic, our invitation to you is to develop a good working relationship with this part of you. This shifts it from being unhelpful to being helpful. We share an exercise below to help you do that. Before you do this, though, remember that, while your inner critic may be draining your energy, it is there to manage risk, so be kind and curious. And, of course, having a balanced conversation about risks on the one hand and "enoughness" and "potential" on the other will give you a broader perspective of what's going on.

Working well with your inner critic

When you've a good working relationship with your inner critic, there's a two-way conversation, a dialogue. You take whatever it's saying and apply some of the sherlocking questions. Good starting points are, *"Is it helpful?"*, *"What am I making this mean?"*, and checking whether the content of what your inner critic is saying is proportionate and appropriate.

Recognising the value of your inner critic in terms of managing risks and identifying opportunities to grow is integral to a good relationship between you.

Enoughness

Noun

The feeling of *"being enough as you are in this moment"*, which allows for the possibility of future growth. When cultivated this feeling becomes a belief.

Figure 9.1 Enoughness

How to cultivate your inner coach

Alongside your inner critic, aka your risk manager, it's important to have a way to remind you of your enoughness and to cultivate your potential. This potential might be something identified by your inner critic.

Enoughness and potential may seem mutually exclusive. If you're enough then how can there be any potential? Doesn't enough mean, "enough, that's it"?

If enoughness and potential seem paradoxical to you, it's highly likely that you'll struggle to recognise your own enoughness. For many people, acknowledging their enoughness, subconsciously or consciously, translates to "no potential for growth".

We invite you to be open to the possibility that you can be enough as you are, and still have the potential for growth. Indeed strengthening your sense of enoughness can set the foundation from which to become sturdier, more robust, and better equipped to manifest your potential.

What we mean by potential here is not only skills and goals, but also the potential of your self-relationship and your quality of life. Cue the inner coach, aka your potential manager. This is the part of you that's encouraging and compassionate.

What are the characteristics of a good coach?

A good coach isn't someone who just repeatedly tells you that you're wonderful. Why not? Well, because, if they're trying to persuade you that you're wonderful but you don't actually believe it, it doesn't matter how often they say it, you still won't believe it. Until, that is, they show you examples and evidence to help you update your beliefs about yourself, which may include that you're, actually, really rather wonderful.

Imagine a coach who is training an athlete to compete at the Olympics. An important part of a coach's role is to help the athlete remember what they're good enough at. They may do this by reminding the athlete of their strengths, achievements, and experience.

With that foundation in mind, the focus can then become strengthening the areas that can be improved so that the athlete realises their potential.

What this would sound like, is the coach saying something like, *"You're really good at this, this, and that. Where you can improve is on this particular part of your technique. Let's focus on improving that".*

A coach will look at all aspects that are relevant to get you to your goal or aspiration. This might be the quality of life or relationships you want to have. It might be skills you want to acquire, or aspirations, like you want to master keeping a bonsai tree alive or change your career. Whatever it is, the support of someone who's compassionate and encouraging makes all the difference.

You almost certainly have many of the skills needed to be a kind and good coach to someone else. Not many of us know how to apply those skills to ourselves though. So, we need to train that ability, which includes using the **ABC** technique to make more helpful **C**hoices. You may also like to seek role-models or guides that you feel would make a good coach and look at what you can learn from them and apply to yourself. This could be someone you know, or someone in the public eye. It can even be a fictional character, like Yoda from Star Wars, or Elle Woods from the movie Legally Blonde. How do they talk to themselves and others? If you could ask them for help or advice, what would they say?

You've now got more insight into the parts of you referred to as inner critic and inner coach. The third part we want to introduce you to is your inner child.

Welcoming your inner child

You may think you're all grown-up and that this means that you shouldn't behave like a child. Well, it's not quite that straight forward. Whilst it's healthy to have a robust adult and grown-up sense-of-self, having a nourishing relationship with the more playful and childlike part of you is important too. Carl Jung, in his work, talked about this part as the inner child, and later Caroline Myss talked about how the inner child part is present in all of us.⁶⁰

The psychological mechanism of the inner child is integral to your health and well-being. As Heraclitus is quoted to have said, *"Man is most nearly himself when he achieves the seriousness of a child at play"*. Or, in the words of Friedrich Nietzsche, *"In every real man a child is hidden that wants to play"*.

So what is the inner child? It's the part that's often associated with experiences of joy, vitality, and playfulness. The part of you that can get wholly absorbed in a beautiful moment and beam with joy. The part that can feel feelings fully and wholly, that falls in love, and that is often described as the source of creative energy.

It's also the part that can throw a tantrum when it doesn't get what it wants. The part that struggles to be patient and *"wants it now"*. This is because of the child's difficulty in understanding time in terms of past and future as these functions hadn't developed yet. It's the part of you that feels hurt when you feel treated unfairly or excluded.

The connection between inner child and trauma

The inner child is also the part of you that is connected to traumas and difficult experiences of childhood.⁶¹ You may think that's all in the past but that's not the case. It stays with you and affects your physical, mental, and social health, even your life expectancy.[62] You may have **A**wareness of these experiences and know there's something there to care for, even if you don't know how to do that yet. For some though, there's also the reality of childhood experiences that you may have no **A**wareness of, but show up in beliefs and behaviours that you struggle with.[63]

Because this part functions like a child, you may feel ashamed of it when it shows up in your behaviour in ways that you or others perceive as "childish". You may even describe the behaviour as "out of character" in an effort to try and rationalise it to yourself and others. The feeling of shame can feel crippling and you may want to pretend it's not there. Brené Brown has done extensive research on shame and has identified that what gives shame its power to disempower you is silence.[64] Remember, feelings are information. When you don't speak of a feeling like shame, even with yourself, you're losing out on important information. You're not able to free yourself from the shackles of shame. This is why learning how to sherlock is so important. It helps you understand what's going on inside your own experience, and speak about it with yourself and others. You can welcome and include your inner child in your experiences by developing the connection to it.

As this connection strengthens you'll discover what you need in order to care for what needs to be cared for, and heal what needs to be healed. When you do that you'll be able to access the joy, playfulness, vitality, and creativity that's available to you through this part of you.

Identifying your parts

Recognising your inner critic, encouraging your inner coach, and welcoming your inner child takes practice and patience. Listening to your self-talk and observing your behaviour is key. Here are some clues to help you.

	Typical self-talk	Typical behaviour
Inner critic	"I should ..." "I must ..."	Acts of passive aggression, e.g: • Saying something is "fine" in a tone of voice that doesn't communicate that it's fine • Deliberately sabotaging something that you've said "yes" to
Inner coach	"Aww, bless me ..." "Last time I was faced with something like this, I overcame it by ...."	Acts of compassion and encouragement, e.g: • Asking for help • Giving yourself time to think things through and sherlock your feelings
Inner child	"It's not fair ..." "I want it now!"	Acts of unfiltered feeling, e.g: • Angry outbursts • Sulking

Figure 9.2 Self-talk examples

At the end of this chapter you'll find exercises to help you develop and strengthen your relationship with your inner critic, coach, and child.

How does your culture influence your relationship with yourself?

Research in the field of cultural studies and cross-cultural psychology has taught us that, although we think that all our beliefs and behaviours are unique to us, they aren't.

A Chinese proverb states that "fish can't see water". Edward T Hall, an anthropologist and cross-cultural researcher, expanded the phrase to "a fish cannot see the water that it swims in."[65] It means that you often don't see the core beliefs and values that drive your experience, the ones that your inner critic is so keen that you follow.

09 Thor has a personal example of this. When they moved away from Iceland in 1999, they didn't think they were "that" Icelandic really. After a few months in the UK, they started realising that there were several cultural differences between Iceland and the UK. For example, in the UK, people say *"please"*, *"thank you"*, and *"sorry"* a lot, and in Iceland, people are far more comfortable talking about sex.

Another leading authority in the field of cultural studies is Gert Hofstede who did seminal research including a number of cultures. His results showed, for example, how individualistic and collectivistic[66,67] cultures score differently on behaviours such as perfectionism. This is then likely to influence self-talk about perfectionism.

Certain behaviours started to show up when he looked at big groups. The behaviours that you would have thought weren't that shared, became shared across a particular culture. For example, how you think about money is related to how you think about the future which is influenced by the culture you grew up in. According to Hofstede, Americans[68] are less likely to focus resources like effort and money in preparing for the future. Germans,[69] on the other hand, score highly on this aspect with a strong propensity to save.[70]

The neuroscientist and author Professor Lisa Feldman Barrett references this in her fascinating book *Seven and a Half Myths About the Brain*.[71] Indeed myth six is that "Brains make more than one kind of mind". She talks about how different cultures have different fight, flight, freeze responses:

"Falling asleep when you're scared might seem strange. If you're from a western culture you're supposed to freeze on the spot, widen your eyes, and gasp. You can also squeeze your eyes shut and scream. Like a teenage baby-sitter in a bad horror movie. Or you can run away from whatever is scaring you. These behaviours are western stereotypes for proper fear behaviour. In Bali, the stereotype is to fall asleep," explains Professor Feldman Barrett.

The reason we are sharing these various references with you is to spotlight these powerful contributors that shape your personality and therefore your experience and feelings.

Which brings us to Thor's concept of Culturality.

Understanding and configuring your culturality

Influenced by the work of Hofstede and Hall, Thor created the concept of Culturality.

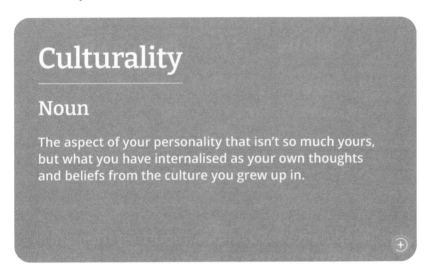

Culturality

Noun

The aspect of your personality that isn't so much yours, but what you have internalised as your own thoughts and beliefs from the culture you grew up in.

Figure 9.3 Culturality

This means that your experience and behaviour is influenced by both your personal attitudes, beliefs, and ethics, as well as the norms, values, and beliefs of your culture.

The good news is that by learning and understanding what you've internalised from your culture, you can identify the beliefs and behaviours that aren't helpful or relevant to you.

Imagine getting a new computer with preloaded software. A lot of it is likely to be helpful, but some of it is likely to become either out of date or irrelevant to you. So, you customise your computer to best serve your needs by uninstalling out-of-date programmes and adding new more helpful ones. Identifying the aspects of your culturality that no longer serve you means you can update your "software" and even uninstall programming that's detrimental to you.

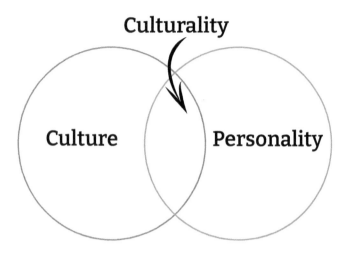

Figure 9.4 Culturality diagram

Why "keeping it real" is more important than always being positive?

Over the last two decades, "being positive" has become a culturality reference, at least in the West. There's a lot to be said for positive psychology, in a "keeping it real" rather than "being positive" way — and actually that was the original intention of the positive psychology movement.[72] Our perception is that the message of positive psychology has become hierarchical, where positive feelings are favoured and negative thoughts and feelings are denied or dismissed. As you will know by now, we strongly believe that "keeping it real" is a far more helpful approach.

Why? Because keeping it positive inherently means only looking at opportunities, strengths, potential, and the silver-lining. You might think this, surely, is a good thing, and far better than looking at the discomfort of the fear or pain and distress that you are actually experiencing. A lot of current self-help psychology focusses on spotlighting the good feelings, and sending the bad feelings somewhere out of sight.

When you bring in the premise of focussing only on the positive, actually what you're doing is ruling out half of the available feelings you have. It's like deciding not to use half of the alphabet. Or deciding to only use the north-south axis on the compass, and not the east-west. If you are not deliberately looking at certain feelings and the information that they contain purely because they are painful, you will never learn from those feelings. This learning could be vital to feeling better.

Secondly, keeping on diverting your gaze, intent on avoiding seeing what's actually going on for you, is a bit like always distracting a child with sweets, or toys. They never learn the psychological skills of boundaries, of assertiveness, of communication, or being able to sit with the feelings they're experiencing. They therefore never learn the skills they need to feel robust and sturdy.

If you don't take the learning from those feelings, you're not able to address the issues they are showing you. Let's take an example of physical pain. If you start with low-level pain and numb it out by taking painkillers, or distracting yourself with "this shiny new thing over here", guess what? It may get worse because you are not addressing the pain. Sometimes it isn't until you get to the point where it's absolutely unbearable and you can't face it anymore that you finally take action. By that point though, you may find that the situation has got so much worse than if you'd actually intervened earlier. At that point you're not only dealing with the original cause, you're dealing with all the consequences of the avoidance as well.

These are the key reasons why we encourage you to practise keeping it real, rather than always focussing on the positive.

Keeping it real also works in the other direction. Just as it's important to look at the negative, to sit with the discomfort, get curious about it, and sherlock the clues, it's helpful not to get stuck there. Having the tendency to always see the risk, or the negative, can be just as unhelpful as always focus on the most positive outcome.

Our invitation here is to practise moving across both spaces. Look at the positive, the potential, and the benefits of any situation, while building up the stamina and skills to sit with that which is uncomfortable. Find your way to what feels real, which is often that third space between the two extremes. Scary, perhaps, but taking your struggles and fears (negatives) by the hand and keeping it real is so much more powerful than simply focussing on the positive.

Why is taking your struggles and fears by the hand a more powerful option than focussing on the positive?

Pain and fear, whether physical, mental, or social, are designed to make you feel uncomfortable. Think about it. If the things that actually cause you pain and scare you made you feel all comfortable and lovely, you would never take action. Feelings that cause discomfort are there to give you the information that you need to take action. Knowing this is helpful.

The crocodile part of the brain, however, does not understand this. This part of your brain is influenced by your senses which means that whether you see a tiger in the cinema or in real life, your fear response is activated. This part of your brain also doesn't seem to respond well when you're trying to convince it of something. It needs to have some lived reference or sensory experience in order to accept it. Trying to convince Lucy that there were no monsters under the bed made her more upset. Showing her that there were no monsters under the bed helped to calm her. Trying to intellectually convince the crocodile part of your brain that there is no threat is futile. It needs to have a look and see some evidence.

Now that we've established why avoiding your fears and discomforts is likely to mean that they will only get worse, let's take a look at how to engage with them. You may not have heard this before, but logic works on two levels: there's rational logic and there's emotional logic. Some of your fears may not be rational, but that doesn't mean that they don't have an emotional logic to them. With that in mind, being kind to yourself as you start to look at things is vital.

And because you always have thoughts and feelings about your thoughts and feelings, you can judge yourself quite harshly for having fears, particularly fears that you consider to be irrational.

The first port of call is not to dismiss your fears or judge them as being irrational. Even if your top scoop thinks they are, there will be some emotional logic for why you have them, you just don't know what it is yet.

Use the sherlocking technique to create a map of something that you struggle with or fear. Follow the clues and identify what the feeling is about in a particular situation. You can then apply the seven clue-busting questions to help you extract the learning and any actions that you want to take from it.

Our invitation is that when you're working with something that feels traumatic, consider doing it with a trusted and skilled friend or a professional.

Neglecting your self-relationship is more detrimental than neglecting other relationships

As we've established, this relationship you're having with yourself is the longest relationship you'll ever have. It's the only relationship that is with you, literally, from cradle to grave. From your first breath to your last, you are the only one who's with you every breath of the way. And so, the impact of that relationship is even more potent by the sheer nature of it always being there.

Imagine spending time with the person you find most difficult in your life. That may be your parent, your sibling, a colleague, or whoever. Think about how much time you've spent in their company. Think about how that made you feel.

Now, take that thought experiment and apply it to your whole life. If you had that feeling about yourself every single day, all the time, how would that make you feel? It's likely that it's not filling your heart with joy. It can be sobering to realise that this is actually the state of your relationship. Recognising that the relationship you have with yourself is equally as important as any other relationship you have, and is non-negotiable when you think about it. Even if purely on the grounds of the amount of time you spend with yourself.

It's also worth considering that when you don't have a good relationship with yourself, you don't tend to do self-care well either. That can be in terms of the food you eat, the clothes you wear, cleaning your teeth, cutting your toenails, or getting a haircut. It can be in terms of when you have symptoms that need medical attention, making sure you go and see the doctor.

When this self-care is neglected, not only will you not feel good about yourself, but, actually, your health is likely to suffer, at least over the medium to long term. This then makes you more vulnerable to illnesses, something explained by Graham Goddard's Kindling Theory.[73] When your mood is low, your body is neglected, your immune system is shot, and you're sleep-deprived, all that's needed is kindling like a virus, to light the bonfire.

Many of the people Thor supports in consultations discover that, although an illness was triggered by a single event, there had been lots of stressors going on before then. A single event might be, for example, surgery, bereavement, virus, or trauma. Many have said, *"If only I had known all this earlier"*.

Still not convinced?

OK then, think about it like this: when you're not OK, you can't be there to help support and care for others who are important to you. That could be your partner, your parents, your friends, or your children. So, if doing it for yourself is not a big enough *"Why bother?"*, use your loved ones as your *"Why bother?"*. Put your oxygen mask on yourself first, for them.

Practice

Ready to invest in your self-relationship?

Exercise 9.1: Discover what your current relationship is with yourself

9.1.1 Describe the quality of your current self-relationship.

It can be helpful to experiment with describing your relationship in four words. When you think of your self-relationship, what four words could you use? For Thor, it used to be "awful, confusing, destructive, and dismissive", and now it's mostly "sturdy, playful, steadfast, and loving". Write down your words so your eyes can see them.

9.1.2 Score the quality of your current self-relationship.

The scale is 0-10, where zero means that the relationship with yourself is non-existent, there is no relationship, and ten means it's great and just as you need it. Using this scale, how would you score your self-relationship now?

It can be helpful to check in specifically with your relationship with your body. Using the same scale as before, how would you score your relationship with your body?

Exercise 9.2 Get curious about your inner critic

Give yourself 15–30 minutes to map how you criticise yourself and how your inner critic shows up.

- When does it happen, is it more likely in certain areas of your life like parenting, work, or body-image?

- What does the criticism sound like? What are the actual words or sounds (like a tut or grunt)?

- Who does your inner critic sound like? Remember that the inner critic is likely to sound like the voice, or combination of voices, of people who raised you or have been influential in your life. Sometimes your inner critic can take on the voice of a public person that you don't have a personal connection to. If that's the case, that's another clue to sherlock. Sometimes the inner critic doesn't sound like a voice. You may experience it more as a feeling. One person described it, for example, as a fog. If this is your experience how might you be able to describe the feeling?

Exercise 9.3: Cultivate your inner coach

Give yourself 15-30 minutes to map how you coach others and how you could apply that to yourself.

- How do you let others know what you value and like about them? Think about those that you are in closest contact with and make a note of how you are with them. How can you start applying those words and behaviours to yourself?

- How do you support others when they struggle, or when they are striving towards a goal or aspiration? What are the words you use? What behaviour do you do? How can you start applying those words and behaviours to yourself?

- If you could call anyone whether they are dead or alive, real or fictional, who would you call? What would you call them about and what might they say? You can have more than one person in your crew. Nicki, for example, has Viktor Frankl, Brené Brown, and Mo (her dog) in her crew.

Exercise 9.4: Connect with your inner child

Give yourself 15-30 minutes to map how you develop and strengthen your relationship with your inner child.

- Get curious about the more childlike aspects of your experience. Connect with memories of times when you feel more childlike or childish. What was going on? Can you remember the thoughts, feelings, and behaviours? Use your **ABC** technique and sherlocking questions to understand the clues. Once you understand the information, next time such thoughts, feelings, or behaviours arise, you can make more helpful **C**hoices.

- Connect with childhood favourites in terms of food, movies, music, and other activities to develop a connection with your inner child. Make time to be with your inner child. Think of it as spending time with a loved little one. If you don't spend time with them, you don't get to know them, and they won't engage with you.

- Pay attention to your self-talk when you feel yourself thinking, feeling, or behaving in a more childlike way. Are you critical of yourself? Do you feel ashamed? Sherlock those experiences and, using the **ABC** technique, experiment with how your self-talk could be kinder and more loving. Write down your more helpful **C**hoices to help you remember next time.

Exercise 9.5: Reflecting on what you've learnt

Now that you've learnt more about your relationship with yourself, containing and completing your feelings, and what your indicators are, what have you learnt about:

- What it was like to do these exercises? Was it, for example, easy, informative, difficult, or confusing?

- Whether it was easier or more difficult to learn about your relationship with yourself than you expected?

- How aware were you before doing these exercises about your experience and the answers you've written down?

- Thoughts and ideas you're having about how you could respond differently to what's going on?

09 What are you learning about yourself?

I am learning that I ....

....

....

....

....

....

....

....

....

....

....

....

Yadid's story (He/him)

Yadid, the uncle to five-year-old Lucy, observed his niece as she refused to go to bed at his parents' house. They had moved her bed into a different bedroom from where she had slept before. She had got it into her head that there were monsters under the bed. His parents, her grandparents, had been saying that there were no monsters under the bed, but Lucy was not having any of this and demanded to talk to her Uncle Yadid.

Yadid went into the room and listened to Lucy repeating her truth for the umpteenth time.

"I will not sleep in that bed because there are monsters under it," she asserted, feeling fed up with the grown-ups not realising how serious the situation was.

"Ah. OK," he said. *"How do you know that?"*

"I just know," replied Lucy.

"OK, how about we have a look and check it out?" suggested Yadid. That was very scary for Lucy, so they decided to do it in stages.

Stage one: Yadid was to go first and kneel down on the floor, lift up the vallance and go under the bed to check if there were any monsters.

Stage two: If Yadid couldn't see any, Lucy would come off the bed next to Yadid on the floor and they would have a look together.

This was a successful strategy because all they found was some socks and a long lost soft toy. It was all fine. When Yadid asked Lucy why she had thought there were monsters under the bed, Lucy realised that it was because they'd recently watched the movie Monsters Inc. Soothed by this realisation Lucy climbed back into bed, very happily, and even allowed Yadid to turn off the light.

She slept through until the morning without ever stirring.

It was in reflecting upon this story during a First Aid for Feelings session with Thor that Yadid realised he did indeed have strong coaching skills, and that he could direct such compassion and curiosity towards his own inner-child, gently helping his younger self to take his fears by the hand.

09 Summary

This book shares essential skills for self-care and good health. Self-compassion is central to self-care, so much so that we dedicated a whole chapter to it. By now, we trust you understand why it's vital to put the oxygen mask on yourself first.

To recap, you've learnt:

- How your relationship with yourself is your single longest and most challenging relationship, making it the most important relationship you'll ever have

- How this relationship is made up of various parts, including your inner critic, your inner coach, and your inner child

- How your culture influences your relationship with yourself and that, as well as a personality, you have a culturality

- How it's important to keep it real and that positive isn't always helpful

- Why taking your struggles and fears by the hand is the more powerful option

- Why neglecting your relationship with yourself can be as, or more, detrimental as neglecting any other relationship

- Why putting your oxygen mask on yourself first is not a cliché.

So, now that you've got to this point, the next step is to add in the final component, your First Aid Kit for Feelings.

Chapter 10

What will you learn?

Why "In sight, in mind" matters (where to keep your kit)

What goes into a First Aid Kit for Feelings

How to select items for each of your senses to go into your First Aid Kit for Feelings

Why space, as in the environment you are in, is your sixth sense

How to create mini-kits for specific situations.

10

Christie's story (She/her)

Christie arrived at work following a stressful morning at home. She was conscious that her work day was set to be equally as stressful. Aware that she was experiencing symptoms of anxiety, including a racing heart and difficulty concentrating, she brought out her First Aid Kit for Feelings from the glove compartment of her car. Thanks to this intervention, she was able to bring all three scoops of her brain online and turn her day around. Thanks to what you are about to learn in this chapter, you will be able to too.

Philosophy

You've now learnt what First Aid for Feelings is about, the key principles, tools, concepts, and techniques. We continue to take our cue from medical First Aid and now add the last piece to this manual: instructions on how to create your very own First Aid for Feelings. First, though, let's quickly recap on a few of the basics of First Aid for Feelings.

What is First Aid Kit for Feelings?

First Aid for Feelings is a method with concepts, tools, and techniques that help you respond to your feelings in the moment and in real-time. The First Aid for Feeling **ABC** technique (**A**wareness — **B**reath & body — **C**hoice) is a rapid response that you can apply in any situation where you experience intense feelings that you struggle with.

If, when you come to "**C**" — "**C**hoice", your helpful **C**hoice is to "complete" processing your feeling, you can put things into your First Aid Kit for Feelings that can help you do that.

If, when you get to "**C**hoice", you realise you can't "complete" processing the feeling, then something in your First Aid Kit for Feelings can help. This enables you to "contain" the feeling until you can come back to it and complete it.

What is a First Aid Kit for Feelings?

A First Aid Kit for Feelings, then, is where you collect together useful tips, tools, and things you can turn to when you're struggling with your feelings. Because you create it for yourself, your First Aid Kit for Feelings will have prompts to help you remember more helpful choices. Your kit is personal to you and contains what is helpful to you. Don't feel you have to use what works for other people. You be you and let them be them.

Why do you need a First Aid Kit for Feelings?

When you cut your finger, you probably don't pace around the house trying to figure out where you put the plasters. You probably know where your plasters are: in a first aid kit in a drawer or cupboard somewhere.

When you're struggling with a feeling though, do you know where to go and find the remedy or response you need to soothe or take care of that feeling?

When you have a headache, you know to go to your first aid kit and get paracetamol (or your painkiller of choice), not a plaster. You know that putting a plaster on a headache just ain't going to work, right? But, when you're struggling with, say, stress, fatigue, anxiety, or overwhelm, do you even know what will work? Or, when you're experiencing pain where painkillers aren't the answer, do you know what to do?

Even if you do know, remember, when you're struggling, your top scoop and group scoop will be off-line. The crocodile part of your brain will be driving your decision-making, and, well, that crocodile part just isn't very good at remembering what helps.

So, it's important to have a First Aid Kit for Feelings somewhere outside of your head, full of tools, tips, and things that you know will work for you when your mind has gone blank.

Why does "In sight, in mind" matter - and what does it mean in relation to where to keep your kit?

Why is it important to keep your First Aid Kit for Feelings outside of your head? Well, "Out of sight, out of mind" is an expression you're likely to be familiar with. If you've arrived at this chapter via the previous content of this manual, you will, by now, also be familiar with the expression "In sight, in mind". It means, if we can see something in front of us, we're more likely to remember it and do something about it.

It's worth seeking lessons from where you keep your medical first aid kits. Many people, for example, have two first aid kits, one in their medicine cabinet, and one in their car. We recommend doing the same with your First Aid Kit for Feelings because, if you need it in the car, it's no good having one at home, and vice-versa. It's also worth considering that, just as with a medical first aid kit, the one people have at home is bigger than the one they keep in their car.

So, now we've shared a little about where to keep your First Aid Kit for Feelings, it's time to start thinking about the tips, tools, and things that it would be helpful for you to put into it.

What goes in a First Aid Kit for Feelings?

What could these items, these tips, tools, and things be? Well, it's different for each of us. To give you a flavour, it can include songs, films, poems, sayings, photos, blankets, fragrances, and favourite foods or flavours. It can also include messages and letters to yourself for certain feelings or situations. In fact, it can include anything at all that will help you to more consciously choose your response to the stresses in your life.

In terms of size — it can actually be any size too. Yes, really. This is because, even if it is too big to physically fit in your chosen vessel, you can include a representation of it, such as a photograph, or an index card with a written prompt directing you to it. One person Thor works with keeps his First Aid Kit for Feelings on his fridge door in the form of polaroid snaps. Just as well really, as one of his go-to interventions, when he is experiencing the feeling of "stuckness", is his motorbike. Seeing a photo of his motorbike with the word "Stuck?" written above it as a prompt, reminds him to get out on the road. He knows this "stuck" feeling finds release there, and that, once on the road, he'll be able to access **C**hoices.

It's good to start with just a few things. Over time, as your needs change, so will your kit. Some things will become redundant. New things and experiences will also be added as you discover them.

The simplest way to start stocking your First Aid Kit for Feelings is to use the "coming to your senses" approach. This means looking at what you need for each of your five main senses. We say "main" because, although you may have been taught that you have five senses, it's now recognised that there are more, including the senses of temperature and pressure. We're choosing to keep it simple by sticking to what most of us know, these five plus the sixth sense, and no — we don't mean intuition. The idea is that you stock your kit with tools, tips, and things for each of these senses. Once you have your basic kit in place, you can start to get more specific about adding and allocating contents according to specific feelings or situations, as Christie did, whose story we shared at the start of this chapter.

To give you a feel for what we mean, here is some more context and some examples of things that people we have worked with have put in their First Aid Kit for Feelings.

Seeing — films, books, images

Eyes are the windows to your soul, or so the saying goes. Eyes are also the access point to many interventions that can help you better manage your physical and emotional feelings.

You may have favourite films that you watch, books you read, and programmes you like when you're feeling poorly, hurt, or distressed. Often though, you may need a quicker intervention that will hit the spot. This is where short videos online can come in handy, instantly reconnecting you with what's important. Images can provide instant reminders of what you love or what you aspire to, too.

Here are some ideas of items relating to sight that you can put in your First Aid Kit for Feelings.

Movies

Movies are a good "go to" resource when you have time for a typical two-hour intervention. They can help you make meaning of your experiences and provide a frame of reference that you can use for your own situations. The cinema is also a resource that many people add to the "Space" section of their First Aid Kit for Feelings, as did Saul, whose story we share in the "Space" section below.

TV

TV series are a great intervention when you have 30–60 minutes for self-care . As with films, they can provide a frame of reference. They can also provide comfort through familiarity in a way that films cannot, because we join characters we feel we know on a weekly basis — or, over a number of episodes.

Online videos

Sometimes, of course, you do not have half an hour, let alone two hours for an intervention. You need something much shorter. This is where online video channels like YouTube come in. This enables you to quickly connect with a person who inspires you, a topic that you find interesting, or just something that makes you laugh, a bit like a laughter supplement.

Images

People often put images they find anchoring, soothing, inspiring, or helpful in some other way in their First Aid Kit for Feelings. This could be a visual representation of a dream or a goal. It could be photos of people or animals that matter to you, or maybe a piece of art.

Books

Books are also fantastically helpful for many of us. We can carry them with us, make notes in the margins and dip in when we can. You may prefer non-fiction books like psychology books, or self-help type books. Fiction, short stories, or poetry may be more your thing, or a mix across different genres.

Hearing — music, sounds, audio content, and silence

Your sense of hearing can be a great source of support. Take the instant effect of music. Literally, within the first few seconds of hearing a tune you can be feeling the feelings that you associate with that specific piece, or with that type of music.

Just as with what you see, what you hear can make you laugh, make you cry, and inspire you. Is there any music that reminds you of specific events or times in your life and as soon as you hear that tune you reconnect with the feelings you felt at that time?

Sounds are often highly symbolic. Some people love listening to the sounds of the sea, even if it is on a headset. This helps them to relax. Others like the sounds of birds chirping, water falling, or fire crackling. There's also the experience of silence. That can, for some, feel instantly peaceful.

Here are some examples of types of sounds that people we've worked with include in their First Aid Kit for Feelings.

Music

It can be classical or pop, it can be instrumental or sung. Music has the power to instantly connect you with feelings and memories. Making playlists to help you access different feelings is a great addition to your First Aid for Feelings. Even having a particular song as the ringtone on your phone can be a First Aid for Feelings reminder.

Remember you can also watch music videos on online video channels.

Audio content

There are so many ways to bring in First Aid for Feelings through your hearing. Consider, for example, podcasts, audio books, the radio, and guided meditations like Thor's growing collection on Insight Timer.

Sounds

Many find ambient or environmental sounds helpful and nourishing. For some it's the sound of the sea, birds, or weather, like rain.

Touching — fabrics, objects, warmth, and cool

The power of your sense of touch on both your physical sensations and emotions cannot be underestimated. What you come in contact with, and what you touch, has an impact on what you experience and how you feel in yourself.

Certain fabrics or pieces of clothing can instantly support and / or shift how you feel about an experience. What you wear can impact how you feel about yourself. Becoming more aware of how you feel in different outfits, for example, means that you can consciously choose a specific outfit when you want to access a certain feeling.

It can be helpful to notice what you like to touch. Massaging your legs with your favourite lotion can help you access a luxurious feeling. Going for a swim and feeling the water gliding against your skin can help you access a sense of smoothness and effortlessness. And, just like little ones often have a favourite blanket, so can you.

Clothes, fabrics, and textures

The things to bear in mind are that the clothes feel comfortable and are appropriately sized for you. Prioritise fabrics that you feel drawn to like silk, velvet, or cashmere. It can also be textures that you touch like stone or wood.

Soothing self-touch can also help you when you're struggling. This could be rubbing your arms or doing the CNS stroking that we refer to in Chapter eight. It could be hugging yourself, or simply massaging your temples or neck. There is also a practice which Thor often recommends called "Finding your feet". This is where you give your feet a thorough massage, appreciating every inch of each, and even the spaces in between your toes, recognising the value that your feet bring. A guided meditation for this practice is available on Thor's page on Insight Timer.

Tasting — food and drink

Throughout history, foods and drinks have done so much more than just provide humans with fuel. This is as true of our personal histories as it is culturally. We all have favourite foods from childhood that can bring us instant comfort, for example.

Why is it that food can be so comforting — and how can you add this in your First Aid Kit for Feelings?

Remember learning about how your breath is your portal to now? How bringing your awareness to your breathing helps to calm the amygdala, which helps to soothe your flight-or-fight-or-freeze response and bring the top scoop of your brain back online? Well, your sense of taste works similarly. Taking time to savour the taste of food ensures you're operating in real-time. Even if you don't have the food to hand (or mouth) at the moment you need soothing, you can recall it, and echo a sensation of the flavour.

When you're struggling, you don't always have a healthy relationship with food and drink. Both can take on a whole new significance for you that you may not always be aware of. Indeed, most people, when starting out on their First Aid for Feelings journey, realise something about their relationship with food. Some realise that, when they're struggling with their feelings, they reach out for particular types of food and drink in ways that are not helpful. Others realise that they forget to eat and drink altogether. Reaching out for food and drink in less than healthy ways, or forgetting to eat and drink, are indicators that all is not well. If you're one of these people, ensuring that your First Aid Kit for Feelings is well stocked with healthy, comforting food and drink choices will be important.

Even if you're not, it's worth remembering that, when your body is not getting enough fuel, you become adrenalised. This feeds the stress state, which is not helpful, and why "hangry"[74][75] is a thing.

Foods

Always keep in stock three snack items that are helpful or soothing to you, as well as the ingredients to cook three healthy, soothing meals. It helps if some of these are based on non-perishable items. It can also help to keep the recipes in your First Aid Kit for Feelings — even if you think you know them off-by-heart. As you now know, when your crocodile scoop is in charge, knowing something by heart means very little. Having the recipe there also means somebody else can step in and cook it for you if you're really struggling.

It can also be helpful to cook extra of your go-to First Aid for Feelings meals and keep some in the freezer for when you don't have the imagination or energy to create a meal. We know people who even have a First Aid Kit for Feelings drawer in their freezer.

Drinks

Taste is not just about food, of course. It's about drinks too. Drinking enough water or fluids is vital to your well-being and your metabolic processes. People often don't realise the effects of dehydration, which, even in the mildest form, can include headaches, dizziness, and fatigue, all feelings that are less than helpful. Hardly surprising then that there are now even apps available to remind you to drink.

Being mindful of what you drink and how much you drink is an important aspect of self-care. Having regular breaks to top up on fluids can be helpful. Having a water bottle or container to hand is helpful. If that bottle or container is something that you enjoy drinking from, even better. In fact, in general, making sure you love the vessel you drink from is great First Aid for Feelings and one of the reasons many people who attend our courses end up having a favourite glass, bottle, and mug in their kit. There's nothing novel about this. Just think about the Japanese tea ceremony and how drinking tea can be a mindful practice.

If you're aware that you've an addictive relationship with alcohol, and have ever sought professional help for this, you'll know that, for you, alcohol is not helpful. If this is your situation, don't include alcohol in your First Aid Kit for Feelings.

Smelling — perfumes, memory-related scents

It's a known thing that the scent can create feelings and affect behaviour, for example, the smell of freshly-baked bread can apparently help sell houses. So it makes sense not to forget about your sense of smell when it comes to stocking your First Aid Kit for Feelings.

Scents are around you, everywhere, all the time. You will have scents that you like and scents that you dislike. Some scents may transport you back to events or times in the past. Some scents might be highly symbolic to you too.

Scents have been used for centuries for different specific purposes. It's no coincidence that there is a flourishing perfume industry and home aroma industry, not to mention the growing popularity of aromatherapy.

A scent can instantly evoke certain feelings and so you can actively bring together those scents that are supportive to you and helpful. Scents can help you feel invigorated or calm. Understanding what scents are important and helpful to you means you can add them to your First Aid Kit for Feelings.

Whether it is a loved one's favourite perfume, the smell of old books, or the smell of freshly-baked bread, different scents will evoke different emotional responses for you.

Pay attention to smells around you and ensure that you like what you can smell. Whether it's the smell of your soap or something in your house, ensure that the smell is pleasing for you. Incense and essential oils can also be helpful ways to access or support feelings. Finally, scents in nature, like freshly-cut grass or rain in woodland, may also matter more than you realise.

As well as these five senses, it's worth thinking about a sixth sense too — the environment you inhabit, or "space".

Why is space your sixth sense?

All your experiences are in the context of the environment in which you find yourself. How you live your experiences is affected by where they take place, whether that's at home, at work, at school, or even in the car.[76]

This became evident for many of us who, for the first time in our lives, worked from home full-time during the global COVID-19 pandemic. Before the pandemic experience, we had unwritten codes that helped us navigate between work and home spaces. Something as simple as coming home from work and changing into home clothes, or the journey to and from work, had been part of our unconscious transition between two spaces. In post-Covid world, you may well need to set some new boundaries to protect the space you need.

Setting boundaries

Did lockdown see you sitting in the same space for personal and professional purposes? Did boundaries become blurred? For some, it led to closer relationships with colleagues. For others, it led to an inability to switch off from work and triggered feelings of overwhelm and anxiety.

The physical space, the environment in which you experience feelings can carry with it links to those feelings too. It can also, in itself, just make you uncomfortable at some level. Looking at the very basics of your day-to-day life, the bedding you sleep in, the chairs you sit in, the desk you work at: if they are uncomfortable, the quality of your day-to-day existence becomes so too.

First things first

It can be helpful to look at the basics to help you set up spaces in which you can feel good. A good place to start is the bedroom. Your bed and the outlook you see when you lie in bed is more important than you may realise. After all, this is the last thing you see before falling asleep and the first thing you see when you wake up.

Using spaces for First Aid Kit for Feelings

Spaces, or the environment you inhabit, also includes places outside of the home or work. Noticing and being aware of what places feel supportive in different situations can help you remember them and use them. For some people, places like a gym can be motivating, although it may have the opposite effect on someone else. It's important to be curious about what works for you and not to make a judgement based on what works for others.

It's also helpful to think about the spaces in which you can access different helpful feelings. For example, the gym for motivation, your place of worship for connecting to meaning, places of nature to connect to a feeling that time is cyclical and all things pass.

Thinking about how to sequence these spaces is important too. Sometimes, for example, after you have experienced a shock, going straight to your relaxation or motivational space will not work. First, you need to find your feet again, and access your body and your brain, before taking yourself to your place of relaxation or contemplation. Saul understood this when he found himself experiencing a PTSD-linked flashback on his way home from a meeting in London.

Saul's sequencing space story

For Saul, the cinema is the named space to go to for escapism in his First Aid Kit for Feelings. So, it was lucky for him that he was close to a cinema when, on his way home from a London business trip, he experienced a PTSD flashback. He first watched a war movie and then, afterwards, he watched a feel-good movie. Sequencing the movies in this order helped him to meet the feelings he was experiencing, metaphorically lancing the boil before applying a dressing to the wound. He left the cinema and got home safely. *"If I had not done my First Aid for Feelings, and hadn't been aware of the power of this space for me, who knows what might have happened that day?"* says Saul.

So, now you've got the method for stocking your kit, and some ideas of what to stock it with, let's think about specific situations you might struggle with in the future. Creating mini-kits for such situations can be helpful.

How can you create mini-kits for specific situations?

Some people even have different medical first aid kits for different scenarios: a burns kit, a cut kit, an aches and pains kit, and even a sporting injury kit that they might keep in their gym bag, for example. It's worth creating First Aid Kit for Feelings for specific situations too. The kits you need will be very specific to you. If you know you always struggle when the in-laws come for Christmas, for example, you could create a kit especially for that situation. Or, maybe going to the dentist is a real trigger for you? If so, a dentist visit kit might be very helpful.

Things to consider when planning your mini-kits include:

- How do you feel now when this situation arises?
- How would you like to feel in the future when this situation arises?
- What would be realistic to feel when this situation next arises?

This third consideration is a caveat to the first two, because First Aid for Feelings is only intended to deal with the situation itself, not with the underlying cause of the feelings the situation is triggering. If you now feel terrified and would like to feel wholly comfortable and at ease, it's unlikely to happen immediately using just First Aid for Feelings. However, if you employ some sherlocking, it could be that, in time, you can deal with the triggers too, and move from feeling "terrified" to "possibly confident" to "wholly at ease". How does that sound?

Practice

There are no exercises in this chapter, because the recommendation is to start putting your own kit together using the references and examples we've shared here.

Christie's story (She/her)

Christie arrived at work following a stressful morning at home. She became **A**ware that the thought of doing work she wished she'd declined was feeding her feeling of anxiety. Coming to her **B**reath and body using the 5/7 breathing technique, Christie managed to bring her heart rate down and wiggle her toes. Recognising that she was experiencing symptoms of anxiety, including a racing heart and difficulty concentrating, she reached for her First Aid Kit for Feelings from the car's glove-compartment. She always kept one here, as well as the main one at home.

Opening her First Aid Kit for Feelings, Christie reached for an index card where she had written First Aid for Anxiety. On it, she saw the words "Anxiety Playlist" and she immediately felt calmer.

She put on her headset and walked into the office listening to the song on her anxiety playlist she had labelled "For when I need to set a boundary". It was Thea Gilmore's "Don't Dim Your Light For Anyone".

Because of the sherlocking Christie had done before she knew she would sometimes get stuck in feeling inadequate if she wasn't able to say yes to requests. This was particularly difficult with colleagues regardless of how much she had in her triangle and even if there was no way she could fit in the additional task. The song, and especially the line "I know you and you're enough", helped Christie remember that it was OK to negotiate and set boundaries.

Upon arriving at her desk, where a colleague was waiting to speak to her about the task that was causing her anxiety, Christie's **C**hoice was to respond calmly. Holding her head up high, she smiled and said, *"About that task ..."*. She explained why she could not take on this task on this occasion using the task, time, and resources triangle. Her colleague understood and reallocated the task to someone else.

Christie realised that it was becoming easier and easier to negotiate like this. This was because each time she did so, she was providing the crocodile part of her brain with the evidence it needed to trust that it was OK to be assertive.

10 Summary

So that's it, everything you need to know about the First Aid for Feelings approach, including how to build your own First Aid Kit for Feelings!

Hopefully, you are now confident that, whatever you're feeling, you can use your First Aid for Feelings to help you feel better within yourself and about yourself.

Hopefully, you've all the knowledge you need to build your own, highly-personalised First Aid Kit for Feelings too.

Let's recap on the key learning from this chapter.

You've learnt:

· That "in sight" means "in mind" and that keeping your First Aid Kit for Feelings in a visible place can help you when you begin to struggle

· That having something to appeal to all six of your senses in your First Aid Kit for Feelings will set you up for success, no matter what life throws at you

· How to select items for each of your senses to go into your First Aid Kit for Feelings

· That "space", or the environment you are in, is your sixth sense. And including spaces that help you feel how you want to in your kit is as important as including items to help ease your other five senses

· How to create mini-kits for specific situations.

You're now ready to start putting all of your learning together. In doing so, you will come to understand that self-care is actually the kindest thing you can do for those you love. You will also learn how to create the conditions you need to help you move well through challenging times.

Chapter 11

What will you do?

You will clarify your own evolving story

You will clarify your "Why bother?"

You will become aware of what's likely to get in your way

You will set yourself up well to sustain your evolving self-care practice.

11

Your story

In every chapter of this manual so far, we've started with a story. We're not doing that here. This is because our invitation for you now is to write your own story.

In every other chapter, we've presented to you a list of what you will learn in that chapter. We're not doing that here either. This is because our invitation for you now is to start putting all your learning into action.

Yup, it's time to start doing your First Aid for Feelings ...

What will you do?

· You will clarify your own evolving story

· You will clarify your "Why bother?"

· You will become aware of what's likely to get in your way

· You will set yourself up well to sustain your evolving self-care practice.

So, what's your story

It's time for you to capture your own story in your own words.

Think about an instance where you've already applied something from this manual to a feeling you've experienced.

How would you describe that in one or two sentences?

HINT: This would be the equivalent of the summary that you see at the start of each previous chapter.

....

....

....

....

11

....

....

....

....

Next, taking this a step further, how would you describe that in more detail? Could you write a description of what was going on, what you would have done before, and what you've now done differently? How would you describe what you've learnt?

HINT: Extracting that information from your own experience gives you evidence that this is something that's genuinely helpful to you and therefore is something that is worth investing your time in.

And remember, the top scoop part of your brain will get that this is a good idea. The crocodile part of your brain may need proof that this is worth changing habits for, possibly habits that you've had for a lifetime.

....

....

....

....

....

....

Why bother?

Remember when we talked about your "Why bother?" in Chapter one? This is where your "Why bother?" charts your direction. It's like a north star that you can use to navigate when you're making **C**hoices. Do you continue to do things the way you've always done them, or do you invest the effort to change?

What makes it worth the effort is your "Why bother?". So, what would be your "Why bother?" now? Now that you've read everything that you've read, you've learnt everything that you've learnt, you're at a crossroads.

Do you continue doing what you've always done, getting what you've always got? Or, like Neo in the 1999 movie The Matrix,[77] do you choose the red pilll?[78] Although we're not expecting you to have a Neo-like transformation, we are inviting you to a transformation of a kind, a transformation of the relationship between "you" and "you".

Which **C**hoice will you take?

You now have a **C**hoice. This manual could be just another helpful book that sits on your bookshelf collecting dust. Or, it can be a working manual that you use regularly and frequently to improve and strengthen your self-relationship. It can be your go-to manual to hone your essential skills for self-care and good health. It can help you feel better.

So what's the evidence showing you of how you've been doing things so far? Are there aspects in your current self-relationship that you'd like to understand better, improve, or change? Why? What is it about the way you feel about yourself now that's difficult, challenging, or limiting? What about other aspects of your experience, for example, dynamics with other people, or past experiences, that still affect you?

Now, imagine nothing changing for the next week, the next month, next year, next decade, to your last breath? How does that feel?

....

....

11 ....

....

....

....

....

....

....

....

....

Do you want that feeling?

What could be the alternative?

Now, bring to mind the evidence you already have of what's been helpful about what you've learnt from this manual so far. How does that feel? Imagine gradually and incrementally strengthening that feeling until it's the feeling you have more and more of the time. Imagine what it will feel like when you can describe your self-relationship in four loving and caring words (if helpful, refer to Exercise 9.1.1 in Chapter nine). How does that feel?

Comparing those two futures, which one do you choose?

If this stuff was easy, you'd have done it already. Mastering your First Aid for Feelings takes practice and patience, it takes curiosity and compassion, and most importantly, it takes a "Why bother?"

It can take a while to craft your "Why bother"; that's to be expected. You may start with one and realise it's not quite strong enough to help you make a different **C**hoice to the **C**hoice you've historically made. You may find that tweaking it a bit is enough, or that it's more helpful to sherlock a new one. This is not about getting it perfect, it's about getting it started. So, with that in mind, what might be your "Why bother?"

....

....

....

....

....

....

....

....

....

....

....

Now that you've got your "Why bother?", your north star, your reference for when you're struggling to do your First Aid for Feelings, let's look at what's likely to get in your way.

11 What's likely to get in your way

The three key obstacles that most of us struggle with are overwhelm, feeling stuck, and beliefs about ourselves and others.

Overwhelm

This is when you feel that there are so many aspects that you want to improve or change that it's difficult to get started. It feels insurmountable, like there's this big mountain to climb. You feel like the scale of the changes you anticipate is such that you can't even get a foothold to start.

Step away from the mountain metaphor for a minute, and experiment with a metaphor of a stone with a hole in it.[79] That hole has come into being because of the drip, drip, drip of water gradually and incrementally eroding the stone's centre. Although each drop may seem insignificant, every single drop mattered, and every single drop counted towards making this change happen. Something as soft as water can shape something as hard as stone. Water shapes stone.

And so, bringing that metaphor to the practical reality of your day, our invitation is for you to start with what feels least challenging and easiest to practise with. Do this, and you will discover that gradually every helpful Choice[80] moves you towards feeling better.

Feeling stuck

Feeling stuck is an uncomfortable feeling, and, in terms of First Aid for Feelings, it can show up when you're struggling to find a more helpful Choice. Most people feel stuck when they begin to practise creating more helpful Choices. This is because of your neural pathways, and how they work. Remember the London versus New York cab drivers we talked about in Chapter seven? Because the more helpful Choice is new to you, you've not yet got the neural pathways for it. If you did, you'd already be doing the more helpful Choice.

So, remember to be kind and patient with yourself here. The clues to your more helpful Choice, will be in your feeling charts and profiles. They will be in your maps and patterns. Use your seven clue-busting sherlocking questions and you'll discover your more helpful Choice.

Because you haven't thought these thoughts before, it can sometimes be hard to do this on your own. Asking trusted friends to do the questions with you can make this process easier. Sometimes, working with a professional is needed to help you get unstuck and find your way.

Beliefs

What you believe about yourself and others directly affects your ability to follow through with your aspiration of improving your self-relationship. Most of us have inherited the cultural belief that self-care is selfish, and therefore it's likely that you have some unhelpful beliefs about you taking time for yourself. This means prioritising time to do your own First Aid for Feelings will feel problematic. Despite your best intentions it becomes one of those things that always drops down to the bottom of your list.

It's also likely that you'll have some beliefs about whether it's possible to change or how long it may take to make changes. Do you believe that you can't teach an old dog new tricks? Or that, because you've been doing something for years, it's going to take years to change?

The key here is to recognise that beliefs create patterns of behaviour where you're continuously being pulled back to always doing what you always did. Sherlocking such beliefs will help you tackle this obstacle. Remember the quote "a fish cannot see the water that it swims in" … Bear in mind that you almost certainly will need help from others to see different perspectives, and update your beliefs to something more helpful.

Mindful of potential obstacles that may get in your way, let's look at how to set yourself up well to put into practice what you are learning. The aspiration and aim here is to help you become skilled at your First Aid for Feelings, and feel the benefits of a nourishing self-relationship.

Setting you up well

Self-care and First Aid for Feelings are relevant at any given time as a set of skills. And, like with any skill, practice makes it possible. The most effective way of practising a skill is to bring it into your everyday life. It's about making it a habit.

11 Habits form a huge part of our every day. A study[81] found that habits account for 40 percent of our daily activities. Whether it's washing your hands, brushing your teeth, or even which side of the bed you sleep on, habits are involved.

Habits are a way of automating a behaviour, including the behaviour of checking in with yourself and applying, for example, the **ABC** technique. What you want to do is to harness the power of your existing habits to embed your new habit of practising your First Aid for Feelings.

Coupling new habits to existing ones

We take inspiration from Ivan Pavlov's theory of classical conditioning,[82] where you couple together an existing habit with your new habit. You may be familiar with his experiments on dogs where he coupled together ringing a bell with giving dogs food. Over time the dogs associated the sound of the bell with food and started to show physical responses like salivating when the bell sounded even if there wasn't food around. In your case, the existing habit is the stimulus and your new habit is the response. In NLP this is an example of something referred to as an anchor, where you anchor one thing to another.[83]

Here are some specific examples

Brushing teeth and ABC technique

In this coupling of existing and new habits, you train yourself to check in with yourself using the **ABC** technique when you're brushing your teeth. As most of us brush our teeth a couple of times a day, this gives you an opportunity to apply the technique during this activity. The recommended duration for brushing your teeth is two minutes,[84] which gives you ample time to go through each of the steps of the **ABC** technique.

Saturdays and sherlocking

In this coupling of a particular day with sherlocking, you can train yourself to have a regular self-date to check in about your week. It can be helpful to add in an additional conditioning or association in terms of where you do this. It could be in your favourite chair, or it could be that you go to a particular place like a cafe, so the cafe becomes another anchor reference.

Starting your day and journaling

In this coupling you bring together a particular time of day and the activity of journaling. This is the act of writing down how you're feeling and what's going on for you. Journaling has been proven to have various health benefits[85] and is a great way of "downloading" what's going on for you. As you read what you've written you've got another perspective allowing you to see your experience differently. You could also add in another coupling, like relaxation, so you start with a guided relaxation and then do your journaling. This has been shown to increase emotional literacy.[86]

Julia Cameron in her book *The Artist's Way*[87] teaches the method of Morning Pages where, each morning, you write a few pages. This is a type of journaling that many have found helpful.

When you couple together an existing habit, activity, or a specific time of day with what you're learning you're much more likely to succeed. Whether it's one of the tools, techniques, or concepts you're learning, embedding it in your day is the key. Even just having this manual next to your kettle, so everytime you wait for the kettle to boil, you open it at random, is a form of coupling.

In sight, in mind

Remember this phrase? This is the key component of embedding a new habit and behaviour. It could so easily be "Out of sight, out of mind", so here the invitation is to actively put prompts somewhere where you can see them. This could be, for example, a post-it note next to your toothpaste to remind you to do the **ABC** technique while brushing your teeth. If you're more inclined to do the morning page journaling, then a notebook and pen by your bedside will help. This means it's within easy reach, especially if you place it on top of your something you'll then be wearing, like your watch.

Using apps and notifications as prompts

There are now a vast array of apps available to help embed new habits. For those of us who are more tech savvy, apps, or the notification feature on your phone, can be a great training tool. Setting notifications or app messages to prompt you to do the **ABC** technique (always your first port of call) is a great way of developing those neural pathways.

Make it fun

Play with how you can make your new activity more fun and enjoyable. If you'd like to experiment with journaling, find a notebook or an app that appeals to you, rather than just any old thing. Find a pen or pencil that you like the look and feel of. These kinds of details are unlikely to make a huge difference, but they might just make the difference that makes the difference. If you're afraid someone will find your sherlocking notes, find yourself something lockable, like a toolbox, or a password-protected app.

For your First Aid Kit for Feelings, find a place that's not just practical but also playful or nourishing somehow. Anna decided to treat herself to a beautiful and over-sized handbag that she'd been fantasising about for years. It was roomy enough to fit what she wanted to have in it and stylish enough to look great next to her wardrobe. Because it was in her line of sight from bed, it was the first thing she saw in the morning and the last thing at night. This gave her a feeling of reassurance that she had what she needed within easy reach and was a reminder of her "Why bother?".

Experiments and possibilities

You'll notice that we often emphasise experimenting and checking how something works, rather than being definitive about how you should do this or that. This is because we've found, both in our own experience and working with others, that you don't really know if something is helpful or not until you've tried it. Something may sound great but then you try it and it doesn't really deliver. Or, something may work great for someone but, for you, there's no benefit. Being willing to experiment and test tools, things, and ideas in order to find out what works for you is what makes everything possible.

TOTE and the Scientific method

This attitude of curiosity and experimenting isn't something we've discovered. It's the basis of the Scientific method as detailed by John Dewey in his seminal book *"How we think"*[88] published in 1910. He was drawing on thinking going as far back as the written word. This method of curiosity and seeing what works is what helps us figure stuff out. We imagine that even whoever discovered the wheel applied it. We offer it here for you to adapt to how you learn about yourself and what works for you. In NLP it's referred to as the TOTE model or "Test-Operate-Test-Exit. Here's one version of what this approach looks like:

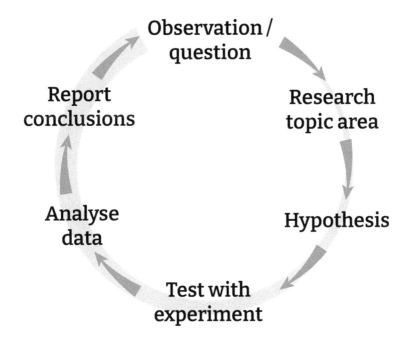

Figure 11.1 Scientific method

You can apply this to everything you're learning and experiencing. Use it to test a new helpful Choice. Use it to test a new addition to your First Aid Kit for Feelings. Use it to experiment with setting boundaries with others. One of the principles[89] of NLP is that "There is no failure, only feedback". Coming from a place of curiosity and compassion means that there is no "perfect" and there is no "right". With that freedom everything becomes possible.

And with all your learning to support this bid for freedom, you've everything in place to fly.

So, what have you learnt?

You have learnt:

- How understanding the purpose of feelings means you no longer get stuck and can respond to your feelings appropriately and move through them

- How to know if you are struggling with your feelings, what your feelings are trying to tell you, and how you currently respond or react to your feelings

- Your **ABC** for Feelings, a new technique which is just as important as the **ABC** (**A**irway, **B**reathing, **C**irculation) for medical first aid, and which will help you respond helpfully to your feelings

- A way of thinking of the brain that will help you to see when the oldest part of your brain is in control. The part that is more primal and less rational. Knowing this creates the possibility for you to be kinder to yourself and more skilled.

- How the practice of breathing mindfully helps to release stress and improves your ability to think more clearly

- How taking time to read your feelings, and what they are communicating, gives you the clues and power to respond better to your feelings, and make more helpful **C**hoices towards what you actually want

- Why, if you feel that you don't have any **C**hoice, you are crocodiling. And how soothing your crocodile reconnects the part of your brain that can see and make choices

- Why curiosity makes it easier to respond to intense feelings and take helpful action

- How being kinder to yourself helps you be more skillful with yourself, as well as with others

- How to start building a First Aid Kit for Feelings and set yourself up well for whatever comes your way.

Our "Why bother?"

Our whole reason for sharing this with you, our "Why bother?", is that we've both seen our self-relationships transform because we've learnt this stuff and developed these skills. And, like we said in the introduction, that's not all. Our relationships with others have improved as well our mental, physical, and social health. We feel better. And, even when things are tough and we're struggling, it feels easier.

Our wish for you

Our hope is that you too will experience just how good it feels when you have the essential skills for self-care and good health. When you've got the skills to respond more skilfully to yourself, others, life-events, and, well most things really, you're more able to be you and you feel better!

You've now got the essential tools, techniques, and concepts to practise and develop your skills. It'll take a while, of course. Like all skills, it's the practice that matters. We know that you'll feel more or less skilful at times. We also know that gradually, over time, you'll feel skilful more and more of the time.

Wonder why we're so confident? Have you ever watched a toddler learning to walk? Have you observed just how frustrating it can be for that little one as they land on the bum for the umpteenth time? Barring any physical reasons for why the child may struggle with walking, you encourage that child, you pick them up, soothe them, and then help them on their feet again. Your confidence in that toddler's ability to master walking is unwavering. You know they'll be able to walk and actually in the end it really doesn't take that long.

The First Aid for Feelings **Manual** is here for you to use, thumb through, stick things in, scribble all over, whatever works for you. There's a reason it's a manual. A manual is something involving humans, i.e. you, and it involves doing, taking action. It's there for you to grab when you need it, whatever is going on.

We're in your corner. You've got this.

Afterword

Healthcare systems around the world are buckling under the load of record levels of chronic illnesses, stress related illnesses, and preventable illnesses. Lifestyle Medicine and Functional Medicine are becoming more widely known, spearheading a more integrated approach to health and well-being, as opposed to the specialism approach of the last century. At the same time technology is enabling us to self-monitor various aspects of our own health, and we have access to more information and knowledge about self-care and healthcare.

Together this has meant that over the last few years there's been a growing momentum towards empowering people to have more agency when it comes to their own health. Self-Driven Healthcare (SDH) is now a recognised "thing", and even the World Health Organisation has joined this momentum by publishing WHO Guideline on Self-Care Interventions for Health & Well-being[90].

Dr Austen El-Ost,[91] director of Self-Care Academic Research Unit (SCARU) at Imperial College London, the first of its kind, says, "... *self-care is an act of kindness, and we should all come together to study, develop and scale access to self-care approaches and to what could help people live longer, happier and healthier lives*".

This focus on self-care and being in the driving seat of your own health is our motivation behind First Aid for Feelings, the "Why bother?". After a lot of nudges and oodles of encouragement from patients and clients to write a manual, Thor got Nicki onboard in October, 2019, to finally make it happen.

We made a plan and we gave ourselves a year to make this magic happen. A few months later we were reminded that, although we're the captains of our respective ships and powerful as such, we don't control the metaphorical weather — that "weather" being Covid. This meant that pretty much overnight the clinical load for Thor nearly doubled and demands for Nicki's expertise increased.

For the next 12–18 months we managed to safeguard a few hours a week for writing time together, but the pace, although steadfast, was slow. Very slow. We then had more "weather" including five bereavements, a couple of house-moves, and the birth of twins in the family. Each time we had to delay delivery milestones we'd do our **ABC**s and remind ourselves to put the oxygen masks on ourselves first, ensuring we were caring for the essentials. There was a lot of sherlocking and re-triangulating. We'd check in with ourselves and each other in terms of our inner critics and coaches, caring for our inner child, and regularly restocking our First Aid Kit for Feelings.

It's all been grist for the mill. Thor often gets teased about seeing challenges as "the stuff of practice" and, yes, there was a lot of "stuff", which meant that we had a lot of practice. The process of writing this manual has been about walking the talk and paying attention to the conversation.

Everything in this manual has been used, tested, and used again, by us and the thousands of people who've upskilled and now know their First Aid for Feelings. It's very much the result of us taking the wheel. You could say its creation has been SDH in action.

We've enjoyed the ride, even navigating the metaphorical roadworks and, at times, extreme weather conditions. We trust you will too.

Resources and references for The Helpful Approach

The First Aid for Feelings method sits within the approach of the Helpful Clinic. We always work with health in all three dimensions of health: physical, mental, and social health. So, when we talk about **feelings**, we mean both physical sensations, like pain and fatigue, and emotions, like anxiety and anger.

If, for example, you are experiencing the feeling of overwhelm, we don't just look at your thoughts and emotions. We get curious about what is happening in your body too. And we look at what social pressures you are under — we look at all three dimensions and help you feel better again.

The Helpful approach is geared towards helping you to improve your health and emotional literacy so you can "read" and respond to your feelings and take helpful and appropriate action. We draw on various methods to do this.

Supporting methods

The methods that inform and contribute to The Helpful Approach and First Aid for Feelings are:

Figure R.1 Helpful approach

Neuro-Linguistic Programming (NLP)

Neuro-Linguistic Programming,[92] referred to as NLP, is a model about patterns of behaviour, thoughts, and experiences. NLP facilitates improving your experience by mapping how you travel from where you are now to where you want to be. As the name suggests, it is about how your neurology (or brain) is programmed to the way you use language in your thoughts, feelings, and actions. Neuroscience shows how this can be reprogrammed and that you can change your experience and improve symptoms of, for example, PTSD and fatigue. NLP draws on Behavioural Psychology, Hypnosis, Gestalt, and Family therapy.

Emotional Freedom Technique (EFT)

Emotional Freedom Technique, often referred to as EFT, is a method of bringing together the Chinese meridian / energy-lines system used in acupuncture with western psychology. Instead of stimulating the meridian points with needles, with EFT you tap on the meridian points with your own fingertips whilst talking about what's going on. It's like tuning together two instruments, your brain and your body, to bring your whole system into balance. EFT is a field within Energy Psychology and applied to various issues including PTSD and cancer.[93]

Clinical Hypnosis (HYP)

Clinical hypnosis, or hypnotherapy, uses methods where you gently close your eyes to more easily access your subconscious with the help of your practitioner. Closed eye protocols help you use your own imagination and knowledge to feel better. This method can help release past trauma and change unhelpful habits. It is invaluable to reduce experiences such as stress (including PTSD)[94] and address symptoms like IBS[95] and pain.[96]

Coaching

Coaching[97] is a long-established method to help sportspeople and business people achieve their goals. But did you know that coaches can help you achieve your health goals? A coach is someone who holds the focus for your highest potential, believes in you, and guides you through, using their knowledge of the issues and pitfalls en-route. Coaching is about spotting opportunities for improvements as well as sharing tools and tips to help you to move forward. A coach helps remind you of how far you have come and supports you to recognise your qualities, skills, and achievements.

Film therapy

Film therapy uses the magic of filmmaking to access your own imagination and insights so that you can better understand aspects of your life. It uses films to support you to access feelings like motivation (e.g. Coach Carter) or sadness (e.g. Good Will Hunting). It's also about creating your own film, complete with trailer, poster, and cast, to process challenging experiences in a different way. Film therapy is an emerging way of working with you and your experiences. Film therapy is not a recognised therapeutic modality, yet. Thor applies their experience from working in film and TV to bring films and film techniques into the therapeutic process.

Meditation and mindfulness

Meditation and mindfulness[98] are practices that focus on increasing your awareness and deepening your understanding of your experience and the world around you. Developing the skill of observing and witnessing your own experience gives you precious access to how you function in your everyday life. This gives you clues to what needs changing in order to feel better.

Thor has been practising in the Plum Village[99] tradition of Thich Nhat Hanh since 2003. This practice informs and underpins much of the Helpful approach and the First Aid for Feelings method.

Acknowledgements

We want to give thanks to our dogs, Denny, Honor, and Mo for modelling real-time to us, and reminding us that food, walkies, cuddles, and sleep are the most important aspects of every day.

We want to give thanks to our teachers. To our ancestral teachers whose wisdom illuminates these pages and elevates our lives.

To the every-day teachers who challenge us to learn and upskill; whilst we may not always welcome the lesson, we value the learning.

We want to give thanks to our families, friends, and allies — thank you for being helpful.

Praise for First Aid for Feelings Manual

Luan Baines-Ball, (They/them) psychotherapist

I've been working for a number of years with a very basic concept of creating a self-care first aid kit with my patients, especially as we think about ending our work, and for myself. This is much more in depth and therefore much more helpful. It has a huge potential for insight.

I can see I'll be adding lots of things to my own First Aid Kit for Feelings.

This manual offers a really clear and useful guide to explore and expand awareness of what we are experiencing, what we find comforting in times of distress and whether we can respond with curiosity and compassion to ourselves.

By making use of emotion and logic in combination it helps us to move from a place of stuckness into psychological awareness through to more beneficial decision-making.

I like the distinction between 'containing' and 'completing' feelings and the idea of moving from resignation through to acceptance or surrender. I experienced a shift when I experimented with focusing on what's inside / outside my sphere of influence. I found the prompts to getting curious helpful as a guide rather than ruminating and potentially getting stuck.

Ann Hawkins, (She/her) business advisor and mentor

The most startling message of First Aid for Feelings is that ALL feelings are information. Getting curious about feelings and asking *"Is it helpful?"* immediately takes us out of an emotional state and into a more logical, enquiring one. From there we can become detectives into our own way of dealing with feelings and find ways to change unhelpful patterns of behaviour.

This seemingly simple technique is explained through memorable case studies that reinforce the theory and make it easy to recall helpful techniques so that effective self-care is always accessible whenever and wherever we need it.

Endnotes

1   Brown, B. (2022) *Atlas of the heart, mapping meaningful vonnection and the language of human experience*. London. Vermilion.

2   We talk a lot about curiosity. Indeed the two core principles of First Aid for Feelings are curiosity and compassion. If you are curious about what we mean by curiosity, check out Chapter eight to find out more.

3   Mattila, A.K., Salminen, J.K., Nummi, T. and Joukamaa, M. (2006). Age is strongly associated with alexithymia in the general population. *Journal of Psychosomatic Research*, 61(5), pp.629–635. (Accessed: 3 April 2023).

4   Cerutti, R., Zuffianò, A. and Spensieri, V. (2018). The role of difficulty in identifying and describing feelings in non-suicidal self-injury behavior (NSSI): associations with perceived attachment quality, stressful life events, and suicidal ideation. *Frontiers in Psychology*, 9. (Accessed: 3 April 2023).

5   The Helpful Clinic hosted an impactathon in January 2020 where 25 people came together to talk about the cost of not talking about feelings. These are some of the examples they all agreed on.

6   Engel, G.L. (1997) The need for a new medical model: a challenge for biomedicine. *Science*, 196, pp.129–136. (Accessed: 3 April 2023).

7   Wade & Halligan Clinical Rehabilitation (2017) Vol. 31(8), pp.995–1,004. (Accessed: 3 April 2023).

8   This analogy is proposed by Professor David J. Linden in his book *The Accidental Mind*. This way of describing the brain has been challenged since. It's not an anatomically accurate description of the brain. We are using the analogy because it's helpful and relatable. If you're interested in neuroscience we encourage you to read Lisa Feldman Barrett's book *Seven and a Half Lessons About the Brain*.

9   Sledge, G.W. (2020) 'A blog on pain', *Oncology Times*, 42(12), pp.22–23. doi:https://doi.org/10.1097/01.cot.0000681568.25609.dc. (Accessed: 3 April 2023).

10 Health literacy usually refers to your ability to access and understand healthcare information like a diagnosis or medication details. Here we are applying a broader definition which includes your ability to understand your own health, including physical sensations and symptoms.

11 Steiner, C. with Perry, P. (1997) *Achieving Emotional Literacy*. London: Bloomsbury.

12   The **ABC** technique is an example of a pattern break. The structure of a pattern break is from the field of Neuro-Linguistic Programming (NLP).

13   Rolf Dobelli's book, *The Art of Thinking Clearly*, lists 99 thought patterns you may find interesting. Dobelli, R. (2014). *The Art of Thinking Clearly.* London: Sceptre.

14   Linden, D.J. (2008) *The Accidental Mind: How Brain Evolution has Given Us Love, Memory, Dreams, and God.* Harvard: Harvard University Press.

15   Linden's work references MacLean, Paul D. (1990) *The Triune Brain in Evolution: Role in Paleocerebral Functions.* New York: Plenum Press. Harvard (18th ed.).

16   Authors such as Lisa Feldman Barrett have presented findings that challenge this model of this analogy for example in her book *Seven and a Half Lessons About the Brain*: Feldman Barrett, L. (2021) *Seven and a Half Lessons About the Brain,* Picador, Main Market edition.

17   This is also referred to as the limbic system but, as Lisa Feldman Barret argues in her book, this model is wrong and she refers to limbic circuitry. Feldman Barrett, L. (2021) *Seven and a Half Lessons About the Brain.* Dublin: Picador, Main Market edition.

18   Smith, B.W., Guzman, A. and Erickson, K. (2018) 'The unconditional self-kindness scale: assessing the ability to respond with kindness to threats to the self'. *Mindfulness*, 9(6), pp.1,713–1,722. (Accessed: 3 April 2023).

19   Eriksson, T., Germundsjö, L., Åström, E. and Rönnlund, M. (2018) 'Mindful self-compassion training reduces stress and burnout symptoms among practising psychologists: a randomized controlled trial of a brief web-based Intervention', *Frontiers in Psychology*, 9. (Accessed: 3 April 2023).

20   McEwen, B.S., Nasca, C. and Gray, J.D. (2015) 'Stress effects on neuronal structure: hippocampus, amygdala and prefrontal cortex', *Neuropsychopharmacology*, 41(1), pp.3–23. (Accessed: 3 April 2023).

21   Raichle, M.E. and Gusnard, D.A. (2002) 'Appraising the brain's energy budget', *Proceedings of the National Academy of Sciences*, [online] 99(16), pp.1,0237–1,0239. Available at: https://www.ncbi.nlm.nih.gov/pmc/articles/PMC124895/. (Accessed: 3 April 2023).

22   John Leach talks about this as cognitive paralysis in the sudden impact phase and refers to the phase when reasoning and comprehension return as follow-on recoil phase. Leach. J., (2011) 'Survival psychology column, the won't to live', *APA PsycNet.* [online] Available at: https://psycnet.apa.org/record/2011-01720-002. (Accessed: 3 April 2023).

23   Budincevic, H., Starcevic, K., Bielen, I. and Demarin, V. (2014) 'An aberrant subclavian artery exhibiting the partial steal phenomenon in a patient with VACTERL Association', *Internal Medicine,* [online] 53(16), pp.1,859–1,861. Available at: https://hrcak.srce.hr/file/186735 [Accessed: 9 Feb 2020]. (Accessed: 3 April 2023).

24   Sanders, R. (2017). 'Marian Diamond, known for studies of Einstein's brain, dies at 90', [online] *Berkeley News*. Available at: https://news.berkeley.edu/2017/07/28/marian-diamond-known-for-studies-of-einsteins-brain-dies-at-90/. (Accessed: 3 April 2023).

25   Maguire, E.A., Gadian, D.G., Johnsrude, I.S., Good, C.D., Ashburner, J., Frackowiak, R.S.J. and Frith, C.D. (2000) 'Navigation-related structural change in the hippocampi of taxi drivers', *Proceedings of the National Academy of Sciences*, [online] 97(8), pp.4398–4403. Available at: https://www.ncbi.nlm.nih.gov/pmc/articles/PMC18253/. (Accessed: 3 April 2023).

26   Nestor, J., (2021) *Breath - The New Science of a Lost Art*. New York City: Riverhead Books; p.144.

27   There's also a third component to the ANS called the enteric nervous system that we're not including here because it's more frequently discussed in relation to the digestive system.

28   Mcgonigal, K. (2013). *How to make stress your friend*. [online] Available at: https://www.ted.com/talks/kelly_mcgonigal_how_to_make_stress_your_friend?utm_campaign=tedspread&utm_medium=referral&utm_source=tedcomshare. (Accessed: 3 April 2023).

29   Guidi, J., Lucente, M., Sonino, N. and Fava, Giovanni A. (2020) 'Allostatic load and its impact on health: a systematic review', *Psychotherapy and Psychosomatics*, 90(1), pp.1–17. (Accessed: 3 April 2023).

30   Zaccaro, A., Piarulli, A., Laurino, M., Garbella, E., Menicucci, D., Neri, B. and Gemignani, A. (2018) 'How breath-control can change your life: a systematic review on psycho-physiological correlates of slow breathing', *Frontiers in Human Neuroscience*, [online] 12(353). Available at: https://www.ncbi.nlm.nih.gov/pmc/articles/PMC6137615/. (Accessed: 3 April 2023).

31   There is so much more to the science of breath and how it works. More and more research is showing potential health and stress-relief benefits of working with your breath. This includes potential benefits of carbon dioxide. The description here is to help illustrate the point about the role of breathing in supporting your stress and maintenance state.

32   This is the technical term for the process of turning the gas (oxygen) into fluid that enters your bloodstream and vice versa.

33   Inspired by the 80s pop-version of the song *It Ain't What You Do It's The Way That You Do It* by Fun Boy Three and Bananarama.

34   Campbell, T.G., Hoffmann, T.C. and Glasziou, P.P. (2018) 'Buteyko breathing for asthma', *Cochrane Database of Systematic Reviews*. (Accessed: 3 April 2023).

35   Nair, S., Sagar, M., Sollers, J., Consedine, N. and Broadbent, E. (2015) 'Do slumped and upright postures affect stress responses? A randomised trial', Health Psychology: official journal of the Division of Health Psychology, *American Psychological Association,* [online]

34(6), pp.632–641. Available at: https://www.ncbi.nlm.nih.gov/pubmed/25222091. (Accessed: 23 April 2023).

36   psycnet.apa.org. (n.d.). *APA PsycNet*. [online] Available at: https://psycnet.apa.org/buy/2021-98211-001Warm. (Accessed: 27 February 2022).

37   Whittaker, A.C., Eves, F.F., Carroll, D., Roseboom, T.J., Ginty, A.T., Painter, R.C. and de Rooij, S.R. (2021) 'Daily stair climbing is associated with decreased risk for the metabolic syndrome', *BMC Public Health*, 21(1). (Accessed: 3 April 2023).

38   Hall, P.A. and Fong, G.T. (2007) 'Temporal self-regulation theory: A model for individual health behavior', *Health Psychology Review*, 1(1), pp.6–52. (Accessed: 3 April 2023).

39   If you feel that you may have experienced trauma, we encourage you to seek help to support you to process your experience. Just like with medical First Aid, First Aid Kit for Feelings can support you with your experience but it can't stand instead of the skill and expertise of professional help.

40   In her book *Healing the Addicted Heart*, Sue Beer talks about the connection between trauma and beliefs. This is an excellent resource if you would like to learn more about this. Bear, S. (2013) *Healing the Addicted Heart*. London: The EFT Centre.

41   A number of authors have written about trauma in this way, including Bessel van der Kolk, Gabor Mate, Sue Beer, Peter Levine, and Babette Rothschild.

42   The law defines coercive control as a "continuing act, or pattern of acts, of assault, threats, humiliation, and intimidation, or other abuse that is used to harm, punish, or frighten their victim".

43   Notice that we're not talking about your relationship with yourself but specifically about your relationship with your feelings. We consider the key components to a healthy relationship with yourself to be self-love, self-care, self-worth, and self-advocacy.

44   Lanius, R.A., Williamson, P.C., Densmore, M., Boksman, K., Gupta, M.A., Neufeld, R.W., Gati, J.S. and Menon, R.S. (2001) 'Neural correlates of traumatic memories in posttraumatic stress disorder: a functional MRI investigation', *The American Journal of Psychiatry*, [online] 158(11), pp.1,920–1,922. Available at: https://www.ncbi.nlm.nih.gov/pubmed/11691703?dopt=Abstract. (Accessed: 3 April 2023).

45   Leach. J., (2011) 'Survival psychology column, the won't to live', *APA PsycNet* [online]. Available at: https://psycnet.apa.org/record/2011-01720-002. (Accessed: 3 April 2023).

46   According to Stephen Covey, your circle of influence includes the things that concern you that you can do something about. Covey, S. R. (2004) *The Seven Habits of Highly Effective People: Restoring the Character Ethic*. New York: Free Press. Harvard (18th ed.). The insight

into "'the circle of influence" goes much further back though, and you'll find it, for example, in the writings of the Stoics of ancient Greece, and of the Buddha.

47   We are referring to chronic stress and allostatic stress that we mention in Chapter five.

48   Thich Nhat Hanh taught extensively on the practice of looking deeply and seeing the interconnectedness of all there is. The focus and emphasis on cultivating curiosity is informed by his teachings.

49   Gruber, M.J. and Fandakova, Y. (2021) 'Curiosity in childhood and adolescence — what can we learn from the brain?'. *Current Opinion in Behavioral Sciences,* 39, pp.178–184. (Accessed: 3 April 2023).

50   Jung, R.E. et al (2016) ' A new measure of imagination ability: anatomical brain imaging correlates'. *Frontiers.*

51   The four main happy hormones are serotonin, dopamine, endorphin, and oxytocin.

52   Uvnäs Moberg, K. and Petersson, M. (2022) Physiological effects induced by stimulation of cutaneous sensory nerves, with a focus on oxytocin. *Current Opinion in Behavioral Sciences,* [online] 43, pp.159–166.

53   Please note that this is not an evidence-based protocol yet.

54   Thich Nhat Hanh calls this your habit energy.

55   NEFF, K. (2003) ' Self-compassion: an alternative conceptualization of a healthy attitude toward oneself', *Self and Identity,* 2(2), pp.85–101. doi:10.1080/15298860309032.

56   Jon Kabat-Zinn is an American professor emeritus of medicine and the creator of the Stress Reduction Clinic and the Center for Mindfulness in Medicine, Health Care, and Society at the University of Massachusetts Medical School.

57   Sigmund Freud and Carl Jung wrote extensively on this topic. Their work has become central to the work of subsequent writers and researchers.

58   For example, *Voice Dialogue and the Psychology of Selves,* by Hal and Sidra Stone https://www.voicedialogueinternational.com/ and Internal Family Systems developed by Richard C. Schwartz: Shwartz, Richard C. (1997) Guilford Press, New Ed Edition.

59   Tan, Y. (2016) 'Japanese missing boy: How did Yamato Tanooka survive?', BBC News, 3 June. Available at: https://www.bbc.co.uk/news/world-asia-36441742 (Accessed: 21 September 2022).

60   Myss, C. (2010) *The Four Archetypes of Survival.* Available at: https://web.archive.org/web/20120529044642/http://myss.com/library/contracts/four_archs.asp (Accessed: 22 August 2022).

61   Firman, J. and Russell, A. (1994) *Opening to the Inner Child Recovering Authenic Personality.* [online] Available at: http://www.synthesiscenter.org/PDF/opening.pdf. (Accessed: 22 September 2022).

62   Felitti, V.J., Anda, R.F., Nordenberg, D., Williamson, D.F., Spitz, A.M., Edwards, V., Koss, M.P. and Marks, J.S. (1998) 'Relationship of Childhood Abuse and Household Dysfunction to Many of the Leading Causes of Death in Adults', *American Journal of Preventive Medicine*, [online] 14(4), pp.245–258. doi:10.1016/s0749-3797(98)00017-8. (Accessed: 3 April 2023).

63   Bresin, C. and Andrews, B. (1998) 'Recovered memories of trauma: phenomenology and cognitive mechanisms', *Clinical Psychology Review*, 18(8), pp.949–970. doi:10.1016/s0272-7358(98)00040-3. (Accessed: 3 April 2023).

64   Brown, B. (2006) 'Shame resilience theory: a grounded theory study on women and shame', Families in Society: *The Journal of Contemporary Social Services*, 87(1), pp.43–52. doi:10.1606/1044-3894.3483. (Accessed: 3 April 2023).

65   Hall, E., (1976) *Beyond Culture*. Garden City, N.Y.: Anchor Press.

66   Hofstede Insights (2022). National Culture. [online] *Hofstede Insights*. Available at: https://hi.hofstede-insights.com/national-culture. (Accessed: 22 September 2022).

67   To read more about individualist and collectivist see Hofstede, G. (2022) 'The 6 dimensions model of national culture by Geert Hofstede' [online] *Geert Hofstede*. Available at: https://geerthofstede.com/culture-geert-hofstede-gert-jan-hofstede/6d-model-of-national-culture/. (Accessed: 3 April 2023).

68   Hofstede Insights. (2022) *Country Comparison.* Available at https://www.hofstede-insights.com/country-comparison/the-usa/. (Accessed: 22 August 2022).

69   Hofstede Insights. (2022) *Country Comparison.* Available at https://www.hofstede-insights.com/country-comparison/germany/. (Accessed: 22 August 2022).

70   There's a growing body of evidence and consensus of five main personality traits, often referred to as the Big Five. They are Openness, Conscientiousness, Extraversion, Agreeableness, and Neuroticism (often referred to by the acronym OCEAN). Research reference: Power, R.A. and Pluess, M. (2015) 'Heritability estimates of the Big Five personality traits based on common genetic variants', *Translational Psychiatry,* [online] 5(7), pp.e604–e604. doi:10.1038/tp.2015.96. (Accessed: 22 August 2022).

71   Feldman Barrett, L. (2020) *Seven and a Half Lessons about the Brain*, Chapter 6, pp.98–109. London: Picador.

72   Seligman, M. (2010) *Flourish: positive psychology and positive interventions*, The Tanner lectures on human values, 31(4), pp.1–56. (Accessed: 3 April 2023).

73   Goddard, G.V. (1967) 'Development of epileptic seizures through brain stimulation at low intensity', *Nature*, 214(5092), pp.1020–1021. doi:10.1038/2141020a0. (Accessed: 3 April 2023).

74   psycnet.apa.org. (n.d.). APA PsycNet. [online] Available at: https://psycnet.apa.org/buy/2018-27534-001. (Accessed: 19 February 2023).

75   "Hangry" is an adjective that describes the feeling of being bad-tempered or irritable as a result of hunger.

76   There are a vast number of research papers across topics such as the benefits of outdoor spaces, the importance of the designed environment on mental health, and the health impact (positive and negative) of the built environment, to name just a few.

77   Wachowski, Lana, and Wachowski, Lilly, (1999) *The Matrix*, Warner Bros.

78   For context here is a quote from that movie where the character Morpheus says to Neo, *"This is your last chance. After this, there is no turning back. You take the blue pill — the story ends, you wake up in your bed, and believe whatever you want to believe. You take the red pill — you stay in Wonderland, and I show you how deep the rabbit hole goes. Remember, all I'm offering is the truth — nothing more."*

79   This is from an Icelandic saying, *"Dropinn holar steininn"* or, literally translated, the drop hollows the stone.

80   This approach aligns with what's referred to as marginal gains. The power of marginal gains was popularised by Dave Brailsford who used this principle to catapult the British cycling team to success in the early 2000s. Curiosity and observations about how incrementally accumulating the smallest object creates something substantial goes all the way back to the Sorites principle. This is a puzzle or paradox of how many grains of sand it takes to make a heap and is attributed to the Megarian philosopher Eubulides (4th century BC).

81   Neal, D.T., Wood, W., Wu, M. and Kurlander, D. (2011) 'The pull of the past', *Personality and Social Psychology Bulletin*, 37(11), pp.1,428–1,437.

82   Kendra Cherry (2019) Role of a Conditioned Response in the Classical Conditioning Process. [online] *Very Well Mind*. Available at: https://www.verywellmind.com/what-is-a-conditioned-response-2794974. (Accessed: 3 April 2023).

83   This is not to be confused with the anchoring technique which although is built on the same premise is about anchoring specific states.

84   NHS. (2022) How to keep your teeth clean. [online] nhs.uk. Available at: https://www.nhs.uk/live-well/healthy-teeth-and-gums/how-to-keep-your-teeth-clean/. (Accessed: 3 April 2023).

85   Dimitroff. L.J. (2016) Change your life through journaling – The benefits of journaling for registered nurses. Available at: https://www.researchgate.net/profile/Lynda-Dimitroff/

publication/308956936_Change_your_life_through_journaling--The_benefits_of_journaling_for_registered_nurses/links/59354f6945851553b6f3c7eb/Change-your-life-through-journaling--The-benefits-of-journaling-for-registered-nurses.pdf (Accessed: 3 April 2023).

86 Horneffer. K.J., Chan. K.M. (2004) 'Alexithymia and relaxation: Considerations in optimising the emotional effectiveness of journaling about stressful experiences', *Cognition and Emotion*, 23 (3). Available at: https://www.tandfonline.com/doi/abs/10.1080/02699930802009381 (Accessed: 3 April 2023).

87 Cameron, J. (2020) *The Artist's Way: a Spiritual Path To Higher Creativity*. London: Profile Press

88 Dewey, John (1910) *How we think*. Boston: D. C. Heath and Company. OCLC 194219. The 1910 edition is in the public domain in the United States.

89 This is called presupposition in NLP.

90 www.who.int. *WHO Guideline on Self-care Interventions for Health and Well-being, 2022 revision.* [online] Available at: https://www.who.int/publications/i/item/9789240052192. (Accessed: 20 March 2023).

91 www.imperial.ac.uk. Dr Austen El-Osta. [online] Available at: https://www.imperial.ac.uk/people/a.el-osta (Accessed: 20 March 2023).

92 Find out more about research into the benefits of NLP here: https://anlp.org/knowledge-base/nlp-research-papers (Accessed: 20 March 2023).

93 Find out more about research into the benefits of EFT here: https://eftinternational.org/discover-eft-tapping/eft-science-research/ (Accessed: 20 March 2023).

94 Find out how Hypnosis can help with PTSD here: https://www.tandfonline.com/doi/abs/10.1080/00207144.2015.1099406 (Accessed: 20 March 2023).

95 Find out how Hypnosis can help with IBS here: https://www.ncbi.nlm.nih.gov/pmc/articles/PMC4015203/ (Accessed: 20 March 2023).

96 Find out how Hypnosis can help with pain here: https://www.tandfonline.com/doi/abs/10.1080/00207140701338621 (Accessed: 20 March 2023).

97 Find out how Coaching can help to improve health here: https://www.sciencedirect.com/science/article/pii/S073839911730246X (Accessed: 20 March 2023).

98 Find out more about the health and well-being benefits of Mindfulness and Meditation here: https://link.springer.com/article/10.1007/s10943-016-0211-1 (Accessed: 20 March 2023).

99 Find out more about the Plum Village tradition here: www.plumvillage.org

Helpful Advocates

Thank you for your substantial support

Andrea Bulcock

Ann Hawkins

Anna Þórunn Sveinsdóttir

Barbara Inga Albertsdóttir

Birgir Hrafnkelsson og Helga Bryndís Kristjánsdóttir

Dr. Samuel Harry Benjamin Roberts

Jennifer Soran Boon

Luan Baines-Ball

Sigríður Vigfúsdóttir

Milton Keynes UK
Ingram Content Group UK Ltd.
UKHW020033031223
433610UK00011B/122